Shop Girl Diaries

EMILY BENET was born in London to a Welsh mother and a Spanish father. Inspired by Brian Jacques' 'Redwall' series, she spent much of her childhood writing stories about talking field mice. Later she discovered Point Horror books and co-wrote 'Evil Eyes' with a school friend which she self-published in her exercise book.

She moved to Barcelona at 13 where she won her first significant prize for writing and was published in a short story collection. After gaining her A-levels and Spanish Baccalaureate, she accepted a place on the highly acclaimed English and Creative Writing Bachelor course at the University of East Anglia, where all the writers wore stripy tights. Unfortunately, she didn't like stripy tights; neither was she enamored by Norfolk's flat landscape and windy weather.

She returned to South East London, determined to write a novel. She tried out different jobs: she taught English in a language school, made a terrible secretary in an estate agents and temped in a catering firm. In the end she went to work in her Mum's chandelier shop. It was in the shop, amid the chaos of crystal beads and confusing customers, that she began her Shop Girl Blog.

Emily's short stories have won awards, been selected for readings and are published online. She has a Diploma in Journalism, but knows her first love will always be fiction.

Shop Girl Diaries

Emily Benet

SALT

LONDON

PUBLISHED BY SALT PUBLISHING
Fourth Floor, 2 Tavistock Place, Bloomsbury, London WC1H 9RA United Kingdom

© Emily Benet, 2009

The right of Emily Benet to be identified as the
author of this work has been asserted by her in accordance
with Section 77 of the Copyright, Designs and Patents Act 1988.

Salt Publishing 2009

Printed and bound in the United Kingdom by MPG Books Group

Typeset in Paperback 9 / 12

ISBN   978 1 84471 719 4 paperback

1 3 5 7 9 8 6 4 2

For Mum, my fellow Shop Girl

Contents

Shop Girl Diaries

June

❧

Wednesday 25th June

I DIDN'T THINK I'D still be working in my Mum's chandelier shop at 24. I thought I might've gained some independence and be sharing a flat with someone who didn't wash their dishes.

I'd hoped to have published a novel too. Not a best seller; just something half decent.

I read a book called *Natural Born Winners* which said I was more likely to achieve my goals if I wrote them down.

So I did.

I wrote: I want to publish a book by 24.

Well, I'm 25 in 4 months and my book isn't written.

Instead I'm working in Mum's shop, where customers mostly come in for therapy and the occasional light bulb.

'A light shop?' People echo when I tell them.

'Yes, I bring light to the world.'

As if I've never said *that* before.

Then I try and make it sound cool.

I explain how we make the lights ourselves.

But in reality, the hard part, the moulding and plating, happens in the factory in Spain.

Mum and I just dress the frames with crystal, which we string together with pins, bead by bead.

It's a bit like knitting although I can't be sure of that because I don't know how to knit. My cousin, Rosie, tried to teach me on a coach to Wales and I thought I was going to be sick.

Some customers watch closely as we pin the crystal with our special tool.

It's actually just a small screwdriver with a hole drilled through it and not that fancy at all. They look on impressed and ask me if I have a qualification.

'That's a boring job you got there,' Maggie said when she came in this morning. She's an Irish woman in her eighties who's always falling over. She only came in to talk to Mum and left when she saw she wasn't about.

It was dead today.

Two elderly ladies peered through the window for twenty minutes then pushed their trolleys on down the road.

Someone walked in but realising we weren't the bakers, walked out again.

I know things are bad when I'm clinging on to the regulars. They're the ones who offload for hours, with the exception of George, the retired road sweeper.

He remarks on the weather sometimes and leaves doughnuts on the counter.

'Slimmin' cakes,' he calls them.

Mum's been away at the factory and now the doughnuts are gathering at the bottom of the stairs. There are only so many you can eat in a day.

I was hoping George had a crossword on the go and would ask me a question. His quiz questions are the only ones I've ever been able to get.

'The capital of Canada?' he might ask.

And I write the answer on the back of a used price label.

But he didn't have a crossword; he was only passing by because he wanted to put a bet on.

'I bet on a horse once,' I told him, because I wanted someone to stay and talk to me. 'I only bet because the horse was called Emily, like me.'

'And did you win anything?'

'No, it didn't run.'

There wasn't much to say after that so he left the sticky paper bag of doughnuts on the counter and left.

Thursday 26th June

I SPENT MOST OF today wishing I could do something shop-changing, like pay for graffiti artists to spray paint the front of the building.

'Why don't you renovate?' people ask, as if it were as simple as dusting the telly.

It would cost a fortune just to seal up the leaking roof. Each morning I'm surprised to find the shop still intact.

One shop fell down on this street.

It was the Christian book shop; called 'The Rock.'

They've moved into the old bakers now.

We do our own renovations and enlist the help of our neighbour Alfie.

Alfie is the King of DIY and is better stocked than B&Q. He repairs, rewires and reinvents. There is nowhere he can't put a lamp holder.

'If it stands still long enough then it can be turned into a table lamp,' he says.

Mum and Alfie once drilled out real reindeer antlers for a light in a window display.

'It smelt horrible,' he said.

'Like what?'

'Toe nails,' he said, and later, 'like burning hair.'

Because our shop is such a work shop it's always in a mess. My old classmate Petra did a lot to give it a facelift when she worked part-time but there's only so much you can do on a low budget.

Friday 27th June

THE RUBBISH THING ABOUT working alone is that you have to keep locking the door if you want to go upstairs.

When you're pinning crystal you have to go upstairs all the time to wash your hands. There's no point using crystal if it's cloudy with fingerprints.

If you don't want to wash your hands then you want to go to the toilet. If you don't want to go to the toilet or wash your hands then you fancy a cup of tea. And of course, after the cup of tea you're guaranteed to need the toilet a few minutes later, and after the toilet, you really should wash your hands.

Today there came a point where I couldn't be bothered to go upstairs anymore. So I pushed the crystal to one side and opened the freebie magazine that had come through the door.

It was yet another dull eco-edition on carbon free holidays. Top 3 went something like:

Camp in your garden
Camp in your friend's garden
Camp in your local park

N.B If you have no garden or local park, why not buy some seeds and plant flowers in your window box instead. Or why not plant a whole tree and camp in that when it gets big enough.

It's not that I'm not green. A few weeks ago Mum and I thought about getting a couple of chickens in the garden.

We even had names: Margarita and Clucky.

Margarita, because Mum used to make up stories about a chicken called Margarita when I was little and would always fall asleep half way through. Clucky, because we'd had a glass of wine and were doing chicken noises.

'But what about the foxes!' I'd suddenly cried.

They're as tame as dogs and forever sniffing at our patio doors.

We've got a lot of wild life because our garden isn't just overgrown; it's a jungle.

Our visitors include pigeons, frogs, a clumsy squirrel, a fat black cat, blackbirds, sparrows and blue tits.

'Oh how lovely to hear the birds!' an elderly friend recently exclaimed. I smiled, 'Yes, isn't it?'

Actually it reminded me of living in my ex's flat; those early mornings being woken up by the incessant chirping of baby birds and myself at the window with an air rifle.

Good times.

Because that's the other thing about working alone for long periods of time, you begin to get nostalgic about all the rubbish.

Saturday 28th June

GEORGE BROUGHT IN ANOTHER two iced doughnuts this morning. Mum's still not back from Spain so I ate one to keep the numbers down on the stairs.

I can't pinpoint exactly when he started bringing us in cakes.

We've known him since the shop began. He cleaned our street back when it was lined with vegetable stalls.

As a sweeper, he'd done us the odd favour; taking away a black bag or box of scrap. He used to bring in old vinyls and paperbacks people had thrown away. Once he told us he'd found a whole goose. But he didn't bring that in, thankfully. I don't think we would've known how to deal with a whole goose.

A rubbish collection works out too expensive for a small shop like us.

'Fifty quid a bag,' according to the dry cleaners.

I don't know what our neighbours do with their waste, unless of course they're the ones dumping plastic bags on the pavement outside our door.

I wouldn't be surprised; it's not like any of us are making big money round here.

I reckon the hairdressers' are recycling theirs into wigs.

They've a display of them, mainly in a dark reddish colour, except for one, which is bright pink.

'We could wear one each as part of our shop uniform,' Mum suggested.

But we don't have a uniform, there's got to be some perks of working in your own shop.

Petra used to wear a lot of red and black.

Suicide Colours. The colours I'll be wearing when Spain loses tomorrow.

I'm talking about the football; the European Cup Final.

And when it comes to football I'm Spanish, like my dad. So is my brother. Even my Mum's Spanish when Spain plays and *she's* Welsh.

Supporting Spain has never much fun. In my memory they've always lost.

Not just lost.

'Robbed,' Papa always says.

The pain of these losses might've been partly avoided if Papa wasn't always so optimistic. Every year he says we have the dream team and every year I believe him.

In 1996 I believed him.

England versus Spain, at Wembley.

I went to school and told everyone Spain was definitely going to win.

Then came the dreaded penalty shoot-out; Hierro hit the post and Nadal's shot was saved.

I remember crying in my bedroom and between the sobs eating a chocolate egg which didn't taste of anything.

Monday 30th June

I WENT TO A bar in Camden to see the final. There were supposed to be loads of us Spanish supporters meeting there but at the last minute half of them went to a different pub. Papa was going to come too but then decided he was more comfortable at home.

I stayed where I was with an old Spanish school friend, because the pub where we were had bigger screens. I didn't have the Spanish kit so I wore a red spaghetti strap top and a yellow neck scarf.

The atmosphere was brilliant; such a buzz.

I'd brought old tubes of red and yellow watercolour paint. When Spain scored the people on the table behind asked to borrow them and they painted splodgy little flags on each other's cheeks.

I couldn't believe Spain was winning in a final.

'Oh my god,' my friend said, not the biggest party girl, 'does this mean we have to celebrate?'

I shook my head at her in disbelief and broke into a chant with the girl beside me.

I'd been waiting for this ever since I was a little girl, watching football with Papa on the sofa, my legs too short to reach the end.

The referee blew the whistle, the long-awaited win was a reality and the pub erupted in cheers.

Meanwhile my friend slipped off home with the excuse of an early morning.

I turned to the *Spanglish* guy on the table behind; a *Spanglish* guy who, after a few more beers I started calling *my brother from another mother*.

'I'm coming out with you!'

'Of course you are! That lot over there are too,' and he pointed over at this bloke coming towards us.

A tall bloke in a shirt with his sleeves casually rolled up; dark tussled hair and a big smile.

I went over to meet him and thinking he was Spanish gave him a big, celebratory hug.

'*Colombiano,*' he corrected, after I'd kissed him on both cheeks.

We went outside and found the street full of people in red and yellow.

'*¡Los Ingleses tienen Gibraltar pero los Españoles tienen Camden!*' someone shouted.

(*'The English have Gibraltar but the Spanish have Camden!'*)

I was so happy, I couldn't stop talking and smiling to my new friend with the tussled hair.

He was with a pretty, blonde, German girl; the only one in the group whose team hadn't won.

We went to Proud Galleries altogether and when she went to get a drink, I turned to him, and thinking I was being natural asked,

'*És tu novia?*'

(*Is that your girl friend?*)

I blame the beer. I felt so comfortable around him. Even more so when he said, as naturally as he could muster without laughing, that no, she wasn't his girlfriend. That he didn't have a girlfriend.

Later he asked me what I did.

I gave him a different answer to my usual.

I told him I was a writer.

Then I quickly said I wasn't really a writer but that I wrote. And then I said that *really* I just worked in my Mum's lighting shop.

He was more interested in my first answer than my second.

He told me he was a freelance sound recordist. I didn't really know what that meant but it sounded clever and a lot cooler than working in Mum's shop.

Most of us could've stayed up all night celebrating but when Proud closed there was nowhere else to go.

He didn't want me going home on the bus with *my brother from another mother* and found me a taxi.

'So will I see you tomorrow?' he asked, as I was getting in the car.

'No!'

Tomorrow I'd be tired and would look awful.

'When then?'

'Thursday.'

It was the first day that came to mind.

When I got home, my head was swimming with all the excitement and beer.

'I think I've met someone,' I whispered to my shoes, as I pulled them off. 'I think I've met someone.'

I whispered twice, because I couldn't believe it. Neither that Spain had finally won the European Cup nor that I had a date.

July

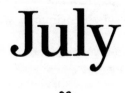

Tuesday 1st July

My date added me as a friend on Facebook and MSN Messenger. 'To stalk you properly,' he said.

I gave him my website address too. I'd set it up a few weeks ago as an online collection of my writing, mainly short stories.

I wanted him to stumble across my travel piece on Colombia and the Lost City trek. To impress him, I suppose, and establish a connection.

'Maybe it's not that I like *him*,' I said to Mum, 'maybe it's just that I loved Colombia.'

She tossed spring onions into a frying pan and the oil hissed.

'Maybe,' she said.

Really I was thinking about that catch up drink on the Southbank with Velvet back in June. Velvet and I went to school together and travelled together so she knows me pretty well.

She knows I lose bottles of water if they don't fit in my backpack, even when we are deep in the jungle with no sources of water nearby.

'So, is there anyone?' she'd said.

'No and nor is there going to be.'

Then I swore to her I wouldn't go out with anyone for a whole year.

'I'm over relationships,' I'd said. 'I'm done.'

It was time to be on my own and concentrate solely on writing.

'I give you three months,' she'd said.

'I'm serious.'

'Three months.'

'Look,' I'd said, starting to get worked up. 'I bet you dinner it'll be a year before I have another boyfriend.

'You're going to lose badly,' she'd said, smug as ever.

That was less than a month ago and I've already met someone I know I want to see again.

Wednesday 2nd July

What with all these doughnuts George's been bringing in, I couldn't really justify leaving the shop to buy a Sesame snap.

But it was lucky I did.

If I hadn't I wouldn't have learned of the approaching Apocalypse.

It was all over the papers.

'down! down! down!' yelled the front cover of the *Independent*.

I went back to my shop and listened to the news on the radio.

'Buyers can't afford to buy! Sellers can't afford to sell! Expect shops to be empty!'

I looked around.

My shop was indeed empty.

Disaster lay heavily on the horizon and it was really bad-timing.

Every recent desire I'd had came flooding into my head all at once. My feet, bored stiff of flip-flops and sweaty ballet pumps, had been crying out for new sandals. I'd fancied a floaty dress to match my new sandals. I'd wanted to wear my new sandals and floaty dress to the park and for my date to see me in my new sandals and floaty dress in the park.

DOWN! DOWN! DOWN!

There was no way I could justify such frivolous spending now. A new era was upon us and it smelt of . . . drains actually.

It was the rain.

I went up to the toilet and poured bleach down the sink. Water was dripping through the ceiling. There was a puddle in the stock room and splashes in the window display.

There's something about rain in a lighting shop that doesn't feel right.

I tried to keep going with the crystal strings I was making but it was hard to stay motivated.

I was really hungry too. I kept pacing up and down the shop with my crystal pinning tool in my hand and one bead of crystal. But lunch was out of the question.

If I thought about it, a panini each day really added up.

If I multiplied a panini times five, then times the whole month, then doubled that for when Mum was in and the times we worked six days . . .

but I couldn't find the calculator anywhere. I looked for it for ages which made me hungrier and even more fed up.

I concluded that in view of the situation I'd have to make do with eating the bio-degradable foam pellets we kept for packing.

We get them with deliveries from a specific company.

Even if we only order a spare glass shade from them they'll still stick it in a massive box filled with these foam pellets.

They look, smell and taste like Wotsits. They probably even have more nutritional value than Wotsits. The downside is they've also probably been left lying around in several different warehouses and been peed on by vermin.

I was resigned to it all, almost.

As I brought the squishy yellow pellet to my mouth, I paused.

It dawned on me that this was not the way it needed to be.

It dawned on me that I'd been a victim of sensationalist propaganda.

My shop was NOT empty because of the credit crunch.

The real reason why my shop was empty was . . .

Well, if I knew *that*, I'd be a much more successful business woman.

Anyway, I bought a mozzarella panini in the end and it was really chewy.

Thursday 3rd July

ROSIE AND I BOTH had a date this evening.

Mine was the same one I'd met from the final of the Euro Cup.

Hers was an Ecuadorian she'd met from the Peruvian bar who I'd nicknamed Mr Muscle, partly because of his ridiculously huge muscles and partly because she wasn't sure of his name and it was a bit late to ask.

My date walked out at London Bridge and gave me a huge bear hug.

I gave him a kiss on each cheek.

He wanted to hold my hand but I was worried someone I knew would see us and think I'd already got a new boyfriend. And I didn't want a boyfriend. I'd told Velvet, a whole year, and I meant it.

We had pizza in a gourmet pizza restaurant by the river.

I told him about my book; he told me about his job as a sound engineer and that red wine gave him migraines.

I said I wanted to write a blog about my shop but I didn't want to write daily.

'Write weekly then,' he said.

'Can you do that?'

'Of course.'

'I thought blogs had to be updated every day.'

'No, it's just better if you do it regularly.'

'Oh . . . I could do weekly,' I said, suddenly feeling excited. 'I could definitely manage that.'

Afterwards we sat on the wooden rocking horses in Coin Square and chatted until it grew dark and the last tubes had been and gone.

Friday 3rd July

PEOPLE THINK I CAN'T be very ambitious. They think I work in a shop because selling bulbs is my limit. They can't conceive that I may have a life that extends beyond our opening hours or big dreams that keep me awake at night.

Even customers who've been coming in and out for years can't place me if I'm outside the shop. I wave at them and they frown and walk on a bit faster.

People have funny ideas about me; they think I need saving.

I was standing on the doorstep, eating a banana and trying to catch some sun when the elderly lady from the posh river flat wheeled her trolley up to me. I know her flat because Mum and I changed the bulbs in her wall brackets when she had the fall and broke her arm.

'You could go if you wanted to,' she said in a low whisper, glancing inside the shop, 'you could leave. Your mum would get over it you know.'

It took me by surprise. Between the sun and my banana I'd been having a quiet moment of bliss.

'Don't worry about me,' I said. 'I'm happy.'

She looked disappointed.

'All my grandchildren have got themselves jobs,' she said, 'even the youngest. She's working in the cinema.'

I threw my banana skin in the bin outside then went back to the door step.

'That's great,' I said.

To be honest, I wasn't as impressed by the cinema job as she would've liked.

'Well . . .' she said, and left it at that.

I could've told her I was writing a book and that this job was the best way to balance work and writing. But I didn't.

I suppose I didn't want her asking me if I'd finished it every time she came in.

There must be a few people who look at me and assume I've chosen the safe path, working with my mummy in the family business.

Like the local alcoholic, a well-spoken wisp of a woman who reminds me of Blanche from Tennessee William's *A Street Car Named Desire*. Most of the time she looks like she's wandered into a fancy dress shop and tried everything on. She'll wear a sailor hat with a gold sequined dress.

Blanche exudes the strong stench of a drinker; I get drunk by osmosis when I stand near her.

A hairdresser at some point in her life, she'd once cut Mum's hair in the backroom of the shop. At the time I'd declined to take up the five pound offer; I wouldn't let her near me with a scissors, not then and not now.

I think she still feels bitter about that.

She came in this afternoon when I was trying to persuade some serious customers to buy a grand chandelier. They were keen. Blanche, however, was on bad form and demanding my attention.

'It must be my eyes! I must be blind! Can I show you? I will show you!' She stumbled over to a lamp and fingered the price label.

'That's just the price for the shade,' I told her.

She went off on a rant about it all being very confusing and trust her to have expensive taste.

Everyone thinks they've got expensive taste, partly because they like the way it sounds and partly because I tell them they do. It's a good way of justifying a pricy purchase. Expensive taste sounds like something you have to treat, like a cold.

Anyway, I turned back to the ladies interested in the chandelier.

I needed this sale.

But Blanche wasn't going anywhere.

It's Mum's fault. She's too nice.

That's why Blanche was there; she wanted someone to be nice to her.

I couldn't give her my full attention because the indecisive mother and daughter were already making full use of me.

'Is there a guarantee it won't break?' the daughter asked, translating for her mother.

No, was the short answer. But I didn't think that was a particularly good sales tactic.

'If someone drops it, it will break.'

The daughter rolled her eyes.

'I know . . . but what guarantee is there?'

I felt a wave of relief when Rosie appeared.

She'd been at yoga and her face was glowing with love for the whole of humanity, which was lucky because Blanche followed her up to the counter and started talking about me.

'She's stuck up,' Blanche spat.

My cousin glanced at me, wide-eyed.

I might've tried to defend myself a couple of years ago. But I didn't feel like I needed to in that moment. Whatever she said, I knew I'd rather be where I was than where she was.

Still, it wasn't the greatest feeling being insulted, especially since I was trying to convince a couple to buy a crystal chandelier. Customers usually expect to buy a luxury item in a luxury setting and at that moment my shop was more like a circus.

They said they'd come back. I wasn't so sure.

Blanche hadn't finished.

'She's rubbish! She just studies all the time and does whatever her mum says!'

It crossed my mind to tell her I actually left my degree unfinished four years ago. But I was mature and kept my mouth shut.

'She's RUBBISH!'

Frankly, I don't know what I'd done.

Blanche wanted a ten pound plasma lamp for yet another friend.

I tried to dissuade her because I knew she had no money and anyway, her friends are always falling over these presents and breaking them.

'She doesn't drink, she doesn't smoke and she's a virgin! She doesn't even *like* boys!' she continued. 'She's rubbish!'

My cousin was giggling out of shock. Evidently she didn't recognise this portrait of purity.

Blanche slapped a ten pound note on top of the small wood table standing at the side of the counter. Mum had bought it from the junk shop down the road and still hadn't decided if she wanted to keep it or not. We could've sold it ten times over in the time she was taking to deliberate. Now Blanche was determined to have it.

I tried to give the tenner back but she stormed out of the shop.

In the end I put it in an envelope and slipped it down the side of the drawer.

I know she'll be sheepish in a day or two and come back for it.

Saturday 5th July

ROSIE TURNED UP AT midday with a latte. She'd been to yoga up the road again and was in her leggings and a green stripy T-shirt.

She'd meant to leave after the coffee but five hours later she was still there.

It'd been another quiet day at the shop but I was happy because the week was nearly over.

In fact we were feeling in a party sort of mood so I called up the local salsa addict and told him to come down to the shop.

The local salsa addict has a few nicknames, my favourite being *White Man Hips* which an old Cuban woman had called him once. He seems to like it, despite it not sounding much of a compliment.

We'd met him in the Peruvian bar near London Bridge when we'd first started learning salsa about eight months ago. He was a friend; it wasn't that I was trying to set Rosie up. Not this time anyway.

I'd taken up salsa on my return from Latin America where I'd barely danced at all.

Who goes to Cuba and doesn't dance?

Me.

It wasn't that I didn't want to. I wanted to so badly. But in Cuba, where the rhythm is in everyone's blood and even the five-year olds dance fluidly, I was afraid of looking stupid.

'Of course you can dance salsa!' the guys had insisted trying to drag me off my seat. 'You're half Spanish!'

But it took a while before I was able to listen to the music without worrying that I'd lost count of the beat.

Anyway, just before Mr Salsa arrived, two young blokes came in and saved the week by buying three big light fittings.

The dark cloud of the credit crunch temporarily lifted and I felt a sense of relief that passed over to Mum in Spain.

The customers told me to pack the lights up and they'd be back in half an hour.

Wrapping up a light is nothing like wrapping up a DVD. Lights are awkward items that scratch, crack and weigh a lot.

Of course neither Rosie nor the local salsa addict were aware of my imminent packing problem. They turned up the Cuban music and started dancing in the middle of the shop.

Meanwhile I was filing though all the flattened boxes stacked vertically in a corner in the back room.

The box I was after couldn't be small and not too big either. It couldn't be square or flat, not wide, not too bulky, not ripped and not the smashed up TNT one which was being saved to prove a messed up delivery. That didn't leave me much choice and soon I was starting to get really hot and bothered.

The flaps on the boxes kept interlocking so I couldn't pull them out easily to see if they were the right size. Then I cut my finger on a big fat staple.

I suddenly felt a rush of jealousy as I heard an Oscar D'Leon song come on which I really liked.

I started hurtling boxes around the back room because I was frustrated.

My cousin and the local salsa addict just kept on dancing.

Finally I waded out of the sea of card with a huge box flattened against me. I stumbled passed them with a forlorn expression on my face, hoping they would transfer their enthusiasm from salsa to packing.

Luckily they did and soon the shop was littered with polystyrene bobbles and strips of fragile tape. The fragile tape is so fragile that it only ever comes off in skinny little strips.

Once the men had collected their three lights, Rosie skipped off to Cost-Cutter and brought back a bottle of white wine.

It felt like we were in a hot country where this sort of thing broke out spontaneously in the street and people clapped out the rhythm.

Rosie propped herself on the high stool and watched me while I danced with Mr Salsa.

'Head!' she cried. And I caught myself and lifted my eyes off the floor.

'Much better!' she said, 'knees!'

And my bottom rejoiced at the liberation that bent knees offered.

I started thinking how I could meld salsa and lighting together, where I could have customers simultaneously dancing and buying. But then I thought about the inevitable breakages.

'I've never seen your *tush* move like that before!' Rosie said excitedly.

That made my day. I took my place on the stool while she danced.

Just before six o'clock closing time, the three of us ran over the road to the new Dress Shop and my cousin and I each bought a floaty dress to wear that evening.

We went out in Vauxhall and danced our feet off.

Early the next morning, our ears still tingling with music, Rosie and I sat on her sofa eating dry pita bread with strawberry jam.

Tuesday 8th July

I DON'T REALLY KNOW how we came to have a light shop.

'It's an anomaly,' Mum says.

It feels more like a community centre than a shop sometimes

Mum and I are psychologists who sell lights on the side.

People come into the shop to talk.

If people did that in busy chain shops the queues would be unbearable.

You'd think twice about buying something if you thought the woman in front of you was going to spend an hour talking to the girl on the check-out about the builder who tipped paint on her carpet, stepped in it, then walked through the whole house with his boots on.

Not any old paint either; I'm talking Terracotta.

The people who ask me why I don't write in the shop don't really have an idea of this place.

For instance, Connie came in today.

Now I can handle reptiles and mud and the great outdoors; just don't talk to me about gory body bits or ask for my blood. It makes me want to faint. When I see Connie a part of me curls up into a ball and whimpers. She's got a dodgy heart and loves to talk about her operations. She's been coming in every other week since the shop first opened

When I was little I found her monologues so boring I'd run upstairs and sit in the stock room until I heard her leave.

'What've you been up to then?' I asked, feigning good cheer.

'Well I told you about the time they pushed a camera up my groin.'

She ran a finger from her belly to her neck.

'It went all up 'ere an 'ere . . .'

I caught a piranha once, I'm not a wuss. But I can't take this stuff.

'They asked me if I had blood in my stools, didn't they? Well I didn't know that's why they were darker.'

I imagined her stools the colour of her curtains. Burgundy.

When Connie isn't talking about her body bits then she's usually describing her soft furnishing and curtain tie-backs.

'Do you feel any better?'

'Of course I'm not better,' she snapped.

'No, I know but . . . do you feel any . . .' I didn't know what to say. Connie doesn't look like a frail woman. She's a big, buxom 60-year old who wears sparkly cardigans and paints her nails. 'Have you had your hair done?'

That softened her a bit.

She patted the back of her hair which was falling out of its bun.

'The doctor says I've put on weight.'

'Really? You don't look it.'

She'd been to the market and her tartan trolley was bulging. I could guess the contents. There would be a steak and kidney pie, a dozen rashers of bacon, a bit of fish, two pieces of ham, one for freezing and one for supper. There'd be something sweet in there too . . .

'Did I show you those . . .'

Cream cakes! I thought suddenly.

'. . . cream cakes I bought last week?'

'Yes,' I said, and I couldn't stop myself, 'both of them.'

After that she told me all about her supper last Tuesday.

I drifted off a bit and pinned crystal.

If there hadn't been crystal to pin then I would've started to go a bit mad. The worst thing is when off-loaders come in when my hands are dirty. Maybe I'll have just eaten one of George's sugary doughnuts. Then I can't pin crystal or do anything useful and when they finally go I feel like I've wasted half my day.

'Then for afters I had one of those cream cakes.'

I thought about her heart problem and felt like telling her off.

'Then I felt so guilty,' she said, 'so I ate the other one too to get it over and done with.'

And that's when I realised she spent too much time alone and it was a good thing she could come in and talk to me.

Wednesday 9th July

I POSTED MY FIRST blog tonight. Thank God I'm only going to write one a week or I'd have to give up everything else I do in life, including work and eating.

I write so slowly and then I delete half of it. Then I get stressed I'm writing so slowly that I write even slower because half my energy is being used up being stressed.

But it's out there now.

No point being precious about it or I'll never get anywhere.

I have a readership of three.

Mum, my brother and the Date.

I would have four if Papa was a bit better on the computer.

Thursday 10th July

'IS THIS A NEW shop?' the man with the church pinnacle asked.

We'd put an advert in a local paper saying we were 'London's best kept secret', hoping it might blow our cover. It would help sales if people knew we existed.

'We've been here about thirty years,' I said.

I detected a trace of pity in his eyes; of course he assumed I'd been there all that time, drinking tea and dusting shelves.

To be fair, I assumed he was an investment banker earning lots of money. I went further to assume he was too busy to enjoy the simple things in life and therefore naturally unhappy, that he'd hesitate if you asked him the colour of his partner's eyes and he couldn't remember the last time he'd bought a chocolate ice cream and sat with his feet in the sand.

I could've given him some history or clarified that I hadn't been working in the shop all that time, but he wasn't the type of person that welcomed a conversation.

As far as he was concerned we provided a service and nothing more.

He wanted us to repair the church pinnacle under his arm that his great-great-great grandmother had bought and had been, at some point, turned into a table lamp.

'It's the main feature in the room,' he said. 'I'd like it done soon.'

I wanted to ask him why, but instead settled for where.

A church had been flattened in Belgium and his relative had come across the spire among the rubble and had wanted to buy it. The builder in charge said she would have to buy all the rubble if she wanted it. So she did.

It was a piece of stone, about half a metre high with knobbly bits all over it, graduating in size. The knobbly bits must've been some sort of flower.

'It'll come to me in a minute,' Mum said, when she saw it.

'They look like rat skulls,' I said.

Alfie, came in to do a day of repairs.

'Oh that's interesting,' he said, which meant he didn't like it.

He agreed that the knobbles looked like rat skulls. He got the black felt tip we use for writing price labels and drew a pair of eyes on two bits of paper and put them in the holes of the knobble; it transformed the knobble into a very cute cartoon rat.

We thought it was a vast improvement and almost forgot to take them out before the man came back to collect it. He wouldn't have found it funny, after all this was the main feature of his room.

Doing repairs is one way of making money while we aren't selling lights.

The other extra service we provide is cleaning. Tomorrow Mum and I are getting up early to clean a chandelier we sold a couple of years ago.

Friday 11th July

I THOUGHT I'D HAVE a proper job by the age of 24. But then I used to think a proper job was working in an estate agent's. I used to walk down Bermondsey Street and peer through their windows, my mouth watering at the vision of efficiency.

And when I got to our shop my heart would sink.

It would sink down the leg of my jeans and roll out the bottom onto a pile of miscellaneous scraps; of screws, washers, chipped crystal, brass nut, ripped price labels and crumbs of old doughnut.

Usually at my lowest point, a customer would come in and beckon me with a click of their teeth and then haggle over a two pound picture frame.

I used to take it so personally; I'd get so angry.

So I saved up money and went away; into the mountains, into the jungle, into new smells and tastes.

In Venezuela I caught that piranha and fried it; it was like eating a hand-ful of toothpicks.

In Colombia I sat in a volcano full of mud.

Eventually I did get a *proper* job in an estate agent's; a really posh one too, in Westminster. But by then it was someone else's idea of a dream, not mine.

'For me it's all about the money,' the boss told me, early on.

'Oh,' I said. And realised I was in the wrong job.

When I walked down Bermondsey Street this morning, I looked through their windows with a sense of relief at being on the outside.

It wasn't even eight o'clock and the agents were all in meetings.

A woman sucking on her Styrofoam coffee cup stared back at me.

I enjoyed the thought that she envied my casual apparel and the jolly swing of my ladder.

And I was soon up it, undressing a huge chandelier coated in dust.

It was the only dusty item in our clients' immaculate apartment, and what a delicious apartment it was.

Natural light poured in through the windows and the crystal sparkled despite the dirt. A bevelled mirror reflected the neatest kitchen with its red agar and hanging steel utensils.

There was a big red sofa in the shape of a tear and a flat screen TV.

I imagined the smooth ivory wall was a cupboard in disguise, because near the bottom was a hexagonal hole containing a cat flap.

I caught a glimpse of the cat.

A silky Siamese.

I felt excited.

This was my future flat.

If my phone hadn't been at the bottom of the ladder I would've shared this thought with my date. I would've taken a photo and showed him to see if his reaction matched mine and perhaps I would've scared him and he would've stopped calling.

Cleaning chandeliers provides a lot of time for reflection.

Cleaning chandeliers is a slow business.

After we'd removed all the crystal strings, we moved back to the less glamorous environment of the shop kitchen.

It's a tiny galley kitchen with one cabinet containing dishwasher fluid and chilli sauce and a buzzing fridge which sometimes leaks.

My hands gradually shrivelled up in the hot water. Downstairs Mum polished the crystals dry.

At 5.30 we headed back on the road with our ladder and bags of cleaned crystal.

About the same time, Papa got lost on his way back from the dentist and called Mum.

'I already gave you directions,' she said.

But getting lost on the way back from the dentist is Papa's ritual. It's because he thinks a lot when he drives and doesn't notice signs. He thinks about deep things like levels of consciousness, life after death, programs for happiness, energy particles. And sometimes not such deep things like the permutations of the *quiniela* (Spanish football pools) or the quantity of sugar in an oat cake.

Then again, maybe he's just not very good at directions.

Anyway, the sun was shining and I was feeling happy.

'You turned LEFT when I said RIGHT!' Mum cried, halting abruptly and nearly banging the ladder into a parked BMW.

This is the life, I thought.

'It's not MY fault you got flashed!'

She was starting to get a bit loud, but still, it was *much* better than working in an office.

'Well, you're going to get a fine!'

City workers were charging towards us in a palette of greys and greys. I thought they looked like the unlucky plant in the photosynthesis experiment that got shoved in the airing cupboard.

My bag of crystal was getting quite heavy and with all the precarious swinging of the ladder and yelling down the phone we were probably starting to look like a pair of clowns.

And then, just as the suited entrepreneurial bunch with their gleaming cufflinks were upon us, Mum did the unthinkable.

She stepped in dog poo.

Instead of being discreet about it and waiting for a quiet grassy corner to remove said excrement, she decided to vent her frustration at my lost dad.

'I DON'T KNOW IF IT'S RIGHT OR LEFT! I'M WALKING DOWN THE STREET WITH A LADDER AND A BAG OF CRYSTAL AND I'VE JUST STEPPED IN DOG POO!'

It pretty much went downhill from there.

I sat on the curb while Mum ran around a nearby park with a mad look in her eye and one bare foot, looking for the perfect pointed stick.

The inevitable local inebriate staggered towards us.

Oh God, I thought, here we go.

He pointed at Mum.

''ere, I know you!' he cried. 'You're that Germaine Greer woman.'

That cracked us both up.

And I suppose it wasn't so bad.

The sun was shining, the sky was blue and as soon the dog poo was back on the ground we were off again.

Saturday 12th July

SO MUCH FOR BEING distant and avoiding this whole dating lark.

I've just come back from seeing my date at a comedy night in a pub near his home.

We didn't plan it; we were just walking past and decided to go in.

We thought it would fill up so we chose to sit on the sofa near the front.

But it didn't fill up, so we were on the sofa near the front with not much going on around us, at a comedy night.

Idiots.

Shappi, the stand-up comedian spotted us straight off.

'So how long have you two love birds been together?' she said, winking at me.

I was mortified. I felt my face turn a deep shade of tomato.

'We haven't,' I cried, glancing at the Date as if I'd just noticed him. 'I mean we aren't . . . I mean we *are* but not . . .'

The comedian's face lit up.

'Oh I think I've said too much . . .'

'It's only our fifth date!' I blurted out.

And then I hid behind a sofa cushion.

I actually hid behind a sofa cushion.

'So why are you here?' she pursued.

'He lives down the road.'

It was like someone had injected me with a truth serum.

'Oh so you're going to stay at *his* tonight?' she said, with another wink. 'Is it the first time?'

'No, no! I'm not going home!' I said. 'I mean *his* home . . . I mean *my* home. I mean I'm not going to *his* home, I'm going to *my* home!'

I could feel my date shaking at my side; either he was laughing or he was crying.

'Can someone get this girl a drink!' Shappi cried.

And thankfully someone did and I calmed down after that and lowered the cushion.

Tuesday 15th July

THE WINDOW CLEANER ARRIVED and banged his stick against the side of the door today.

Bang. Bang. Bang. Bang.

Four times.

I wanted to take the stick off him and bang it over his head.

He did it because the shop shutter was still down.

Our shop shutter isn't electric like the bakers next door.

It's probably one of the oldest shutters on the street. It's grimy with oil and wax and every other substance that's been put on it to make its runners work more smoothly.

Even the mysterious wig shop's shutter is electric. The woman in the wig shop can put her shutter up while she's giggling on the phone because all she has to do is press a button. I, on the other hand, have to ask a passerby to help me lift it up with brute force.

I watch out for men in fluorescent jackets. I watch out for young builders with dirty hands. I don't ask older men because I'm afraid they'll do their back in.

I don't ask men in suits or men who look too clean. I don't ask posh, skinny students because I don't want to embarrass them if they can't lift it, and also because there aren't usually any posh, skinny students about.

Sometimes I get help very quickly. It depends on how confident I feel.

My confidence is directly linked to how good I think I look on the day.

If I'm wearing a skirt I can get my shutter up within minutes of opening. If I've straightened my hair it also does the job. I'll walk out onto the doorstep and seize the first opportunity.

'Can you do me a favour?' I'll say, looking apologetic.

The man will look behind him because he's never seen me before and doesn't think I'm talking to him.

When he realises he grins.

'What's that darlin'?'

'Can you put my shutter up, it's really stiff.'

The cocky ones will try and do it with one arm. They might struggle but they'll always get it up in the end because their manly pride is at stake. I always help them unless they've got a friend nearby and then the two of them will do it really easily.

The other day me and Rosie were struggling to push it up and a man walked past wearing a tight red T-shirt that showed off all his bulging muscles. He didn't even slow down when he saw us.

'What's the point of all your muscles?' Rosie cried, indignantly. But he was already out of earshot.

Other days, when I'm not feeling such a beauty, I'll feel too shy to ask. Those days I go to the cafe, where I buy my lunchtime paninis, and I'll ask if I can borrow someone's arms. Sometimes the young Australian will do it for me and sometimes Michael, the owner.

'You should get an electric one,' people say.

We get endless adverts through the door about new shutters.

But they are expensive and I know we're not going to be here forever.

Wednesday 16th July

MY SECOND BLOG POST has been censored.
I've underlined the problematic areas.

I ask a friend over to my shop to play pass the hot light bulb.
I've never thought of playing it before and I'm feeling smug.
The rules would be the same as the hot potato game but with the added risk of burns and glass cuts, it would be infinitely more fun.

Sadly my friend declines the invitation, preferring to 'swan about a boring office all day pretending to work and being bored to death.'
Pity.
But there must be other diversions to be got out of this lovely, crumbling building.
It's crammed with unusual objects, especially upstairs. The place is swollen with brass, glass, card and packing; it's all tumbling across the floor, up the side of the walls and hanging from the ceiling.
I ask my friend if she wants to come over to my shop and take part in an obstacle course upstairs.
She declines.
I suppose I could speed-wiggle through a tunnel of cardboard boxes in pursuit of a consenting <u>cockroach.</u>
What about a mouse? It might be faster and make the chase more exciting.
Although, frankly, <u>the last mouse I saw</u> in the shop wouldn't have been much fun at all.
It'd been lured into the trap by a lump of sticky Double Decker (chocolate) and promptly decapitated.

'You'll get health and safety onto us,' Mum said.
'I haven't said that I *saw* a cockroach,' I pointed out. 'It's a fictitious cockroach.'
But I didn't want to upset a third of my readership so I removed it from my blog site.

Thursday 17th July

SOME CUSTOMERS COME INTO the shop and make instant decisions.

'I'll 'av that,' they say with confidence, 'an' that.'

Other customers wander in and vaguely mention a lamp they want. Then, like Connie, they digress and complain about their latest visit to the hospital where they were dissected from top to bottom with a tin opener and a plastic picnic fork.

'Look at this!' they'll say, stripping off to show me a ripe purple scar or pimpled rash.

I prefer the customers who browse and then disappear like ghosts when you aren't looking.

Which are not the same as the customers who take months to decide what they want, choose it and then keep looking at it.

And they look and look and look. And they look so long and so hard that their gaze causes the metal to bubble and plating to crack.

In the end I give them a discount.

Like the mother and daughter who came a few weeks ago when sloshed Blanche was abusing me for my apparent purity.

Those two are so terrified the solid brass fitting they've chosen is going to collapse they keep coming in to check on it.

Today they came in with a new batch of doubts.

They wanted to know how much it weighed, how we'd dismantle it, pack it, clean it, feed it and refund it when all went wrong, which they were sure it would.

They were taking it to 'their country'; which country that was, they were reluctant to say.

'Asia,' they murmured.

I couldn't help pressing them further.

'Near Kazakhstan . . .' the daughter conceded, mapping a curve in the air. 'Near Russia . . .'

I didn't see why they couldn't tell me exactly which country it was but I had to keep them happy so I didn't push anymore. I promised to give them new crystal pendants for the light and did my best to dispel their anxieties.

'I need a lie down after that,' Mum said, and went upstairs to make tea.

Their ability to see faults everywhere was contagious and I lost half my morning staring at six pieces of crystal. I snapped out of it when Mum reminded me of the huge discount we'd given.

Imperfections are inevitable. Cast Brass will have bumps which affect the plating; crystal will chip when on display.

Didn't these people have any real worries in their lives?

But later, as I was scanning my belly button for renegade hairs, I realised I was no different. I hadn't accepted body hair was inevitable. Instead I spend ages looking out for it. And I look so hard and so long that eventually I believe I'm Chewbacca.

Monday 21st July

I HAD A DAY OFF and met the Date.

We were going to Regent's Park so he said to wait outside Bakerloo Station.

My phone rang while I was there.

'Get in!' he said.

'Where?'

'Behind the bus! Quick! Get in!'

There was a bus in front of me and a bus pulling up behind that one. So I hung up on him and rushed onto the end bus.

He rang me back a second later.

'What are you doing?' he said. 'I'm in the car.'

He drove after my bus and I met him at the next stop, as red as the flowers on my summer skirt.

'I'm not used to people driving cars!' I said.

He laughed and leaned over to kiss me as if there was all the time in the world and there was no traffic behind us.

There's something about being in a car with a date. Maybe it's because I can't drive so I think it's exciting, grown up even. All I know is, I'd been determined not to fall for anyone for at least a year but in that moment I really fancied him.

He said it later, after we'd eaten our picnic. When the sun was setting and we were lying side by side in silence. I was contemplating the quickest way to meet Rosie for salsa and wishing there was more time.

'So, do you want to go out with me?'

My skin suddenly gave off all the heat of that day's sun.

I was a little radiator. And my heart was thumping.

I'm sure he could feel it.

'Well, I don't *not* want to go out you,' I whispered.

Thursday 24th July

I KNOW MR MUSCLE isn't the love of Rosie's life but he hasn't disappeared completely from it either. He probably should've after the disaster last weekend, when he invited us to a Latin club in the middle of nowhere.

We had to get there by overground train; usually I don't set foot outside the tube map.

'New place, new experience,' we told ourselves. 'It'll be good for us.'

We got out at the station, walked a couple of metres down the road and stopped.

On the corner was a miserable looking pub with a fizzling pink neon sign and a window showing off a collection of lonely, inebriated men. The rest of the street was made up of tatty shops with shop shutters as tired as ours.

'Maybe it's the other way,' I said.

But as we looked ahead, we focused on the motley crew gathered outside one of the shops.

'That's it!' I said.

'No,' Rosie said. 'It can't be.'

'It is! It is!'

It looked like an old hairdressers with its wooden, unlit sign; an abandoned old hairdresser where everyone had decided to hang out for a clandestine party.

It was dark and everyone was crowded around the cars, part parked on the pavement.

Without exception everyone looked decidedly Peruvian.

I suddenly felt very tall.

I imagined the attention we were going to get if we went inside and I felt intimidated.

'I'm not going in there,' I said.

'Maybe it's nice inside,' Rosie said.

But I couldn't imagine how it could be.

Rosie's phone started ringing.

'Oh it's him! What shall I say?'

'I don't know . . . but I'm not going.'

A bit of sweat is inevitable at salsa clubs but even at a distance I knew this place would be steaming.

She didn't answer her mobile.

He rang again.

Our last train back was in ten minutes; if we missed it we'd have to get a night bus which would take hours. If we stayed and didn't like it, those hours on the bus would hurt even more.

We went back to the train station platform and tossed a coin.

'Heads we stay,' Rosie said.

The coin rolled off on its side, spun and then dropped on one side.

Heads.

The train drew in.

'Sod the coin,' I said, and we both got on the train back to London.

That's how I learned the true reason for tossing the coin, which is not so it can make a choice for you, but to find out what it is you really want.

Rosie later apologised for not turning up that night. Still, I didn't think we'd see Mr Muscle again.

But we did. Yesterday afternoon.

We'd just left her house to have a drink with some friends of hers, all of them financial consultants, when he called her.

'Where are you?' he asked. 'I'm coming to see you.'

Moments later, a car blaring *Reggaetón*, pulled up to the curb beside us and stopped.

Mr Muscle jumped out, wearing sunglasses and a tight blue tie-dye T-shirt that rose up to his naval.

Rosie went bright pink.

I didn't know where to look as he went to kiss her.

I'd only ever seen him once and he'd been wearing a shirt.

He'd looked good in a shirt.

He'd looked okay.

But this was something else. He looked like he might have a work out video, called 'Pump with Papi Latino'.

He couldn't come to the pub with us. Rosie didn't push him either. In fact she didn't invite him.

I realised why when I met her consultant friends.

They were all in their 20s going on 50.

All in V-necks; burgundy or brown. Conoisseurs of fine wine, complaining about the free accommodation they'd been given on their last business trip to Switzerland.

They couldn't have been more different from Mr Muscle.

They ordered food and Rosie and I went to the bar to get a drink.

We looked at each other as we stood there in silence, knowing exactly what we were each thinking.

'I don't know what's better,' she said. 'This or that tie-dye T-shirt.'

'I'm thinking the T-shirt,' I said.

She sighed.

'You're probably right.'

Sunday 26th July

THE DATE SAW WHAT I'd written and has started calling me Chubaquita.

'Little Chewbacca.'

I'm not sure if that's a good thing.

I've gained a lot of nicknames since meeting him. They all sound sweet enough in Spanish with a diminutive. You could say anything in Spanish and add a diminutive and it would sound affectionate.

Like *Tostadita*.

Little toast.

I bet a lot of people would love to be called little toast.

August

—⚜—

Tuesday 5th August

EIGHT WEEKS AGO A posh bathroom company ordered a huge empire chandelier.

It arrived yesterday, flat-packed.

If it hadn't been flat-packed it wouldn't have fit through the shop door.

At the time Mum had felt so relieved that our cash flow could flow again that she told them we'd dress the chandelier in-situ at no extra cost.

Well yesterday Mum was back in Spain on a flying visit to the factory and it was down to me to go over there before work and assemble it by myself.

When I arrived there was a lot of other work being done in the show room; tiling, painting, plumbing.

The builder chipping away in front of me looked like a little old hobbit. Bent, hairy and mumbling to himself; he didn't know what to say when he saw me up the ladder. He wasn't expecting a girl; especially one in a flowery top and red lipstick.

The hobbit stopped half-way through his job and watched me dress the enormous chandelier. It'd taken me ages to unwrap and lay out the crystal in order. Crystal strings were spread out all over the floor where soon a bath was going to be installed.

' So 'oo puts lights like that in their bathroom?' he asked, hands on hips.

It was a metre wide and wouldn't fit through the door of mine; so it wasn't me.

'Arabs and Jews, that's 'oo,' he said.

I didn't know what to say to that, it felt like dangerous waters.

We've always sent a lot of crystal to Africa and the Caribbean, although our customers generally buy for reception rooms rather than bathrooms.

If I ever got a bathroom with a high enough ceiling, I'd love a little sparkly chandelier.

The hobbit wandered off to examine the handiwork of another builder nearby.

'Ain't perfect,' I heard him say. 'Only Allah's perfect! That's what they say, innit? Only Allah's perfect.'

None of the other workers had much to say to me. They're always a bit shyer when they're outside their vans.

One of the builders came over and watched me for a while. It made me feel self-conscious though and my hands got sweaty. There were sinks all over the place but not one I could use to wash my hands.

'Coffee?' he asked, which was kind of him.

It went cold before I drank it because I didn't want to keep coming down from my ladder.

I liked the feeling of being part of a bigger project.

I like to see a space transforming before my eyes.

Lighting does that, it transforms. And that's not just my sales pitch.

Thursday 7th August

I CAUGHT UP WITH Velvet and Nina after work. They'd arrived early and had ordered a bottle of white wine.

We hadn't met up in ages and Nina had news. She'd met a bloke and was thinking of introducing him to her parents to get their seal of approval. Her family is Hindu and their approval carries quite a bit of weight. Not that my parents opinion doesn't matter; it just wouldn't matter that much in the early stages.

So we had a bottle of wine and some bread. We had some bread because the restaurant didn't let us drink outside without eating.

'I've given wine up,' I said, and then helped myself to a glass.

'Since when?' Velvet scoffed.

'It makes me emotional. I'll only eat it with food now.'

We ordered some olives and later, another bottle.

By the time I got home I was pretty tipsy.

I attacked a packet of biscuits and switched on my laptop.

Crumbs flew across my keyboard as I bashed out euphoric nonsense on Facebook chat, showering my date with all sorts of wonderful compliments that I'd blush about in the morning.

I made a sandwich because it seemed like the right thing to do.

I was so engrossed in my merry internet world I didn't notice the mould on the cheese until I'd bitten into it and could taste that horrible, damp, green taste on my tongue.

The very sight of mould used to send me hurtling hysterically out of the room and retching until someone, usually Mum, had removed it from the house.

I'm more mature now.

I like to think I'm more sensible about drinking too.

Despite the mess of biscuits and my silly internet jabber, last night I was clever enough to slurp gallons of tap water before I collapsed under the heap of bags, books and coat hangers that is my current duvet.

Result: no hangover.

Last year I wouldn't have been that clever. Last year the night would have ended with me

a) sobbing about *insert a poor country*
b) chucking jewellery down the drain because of *insert a poor country* or
c) declaring my imminent departure to a faraway mountain where I would finally learn to drive and live independently.

Things can change though; you've just got to clear the clutter and let the light out.

Every crystal cleaner knows that. Underneath the dust, the crystal is still sparkling.

Saturday 9th August

I'M GOING TO SPAIN tomorrow for two whole weeks, which means I have to pack.

Packing is one of my least favourite activities.

How am I supposed to anticipate what I'll want to wear each day for two weeks when I don't know what I want to wear tomorrow?

I even want to amend my Facebook profile just so I can put 'packing' in the dislikes section.

If I could be bothered to log in, I would. But I've got to stop logging in and logging off. The time I spend doing that must amount to full days by now, a long weekend even.

Anyway, I don't even know if there is a dislikes section on Facebook.

I just know there's an Interests section.

Maybe dislikes is in the Interests section.

But that wouldn't make sense because you're not usually interested in the things you dislike; that's why you dislike them.

Interests sections are another one of my other least favourite things. It's all my worst questions rolled into one. Dislikes, I could do.

Dislikes:

Packing

Filling Interest Sections (specifically the question: What's your favourite music?)

Filling forms in general

Airport Controls (specifically people confiscating my tweezers and telling me to take my shoes off, especially if I've thoughtlessly put on my boxer boots which take three weeks to take off and three weeks to put on . . . and oh, I've missed the plane.)

Giving Refunds

Washing lettuce

Full Cream Milk (makes me want to gag)

The Date telling me Semi-Skimmed Milk isn't real milk (it is)

People talking about Detox diets (it's boring).

But packing is the one I feel most strongly about. I just refuse to do it.

I have a whole evening free and I don't do it.

I muck about; I make lists of my dislikes.

I do everything I can to not pack.

And then it gets to midnight and I start to feel the inklings of panic.

Some people feel excited when they pack because it means they're going on holiday.

I get excited when I'm on the plane.

When I'm on the plane I know I've finished packing.

August — who knows what day it is? I'm on holiday!

'*No pasa nada . . .*' my brother's friend, Cookie, said with a shrug.

He pushed back his dreadlocks and settled cross-legged on the gritty sand because he had no towel. '*Es Agosto!*'

That was the answer to everything. It's all good, it's August!

Shops shut, businesses close, factories turn off their machinery. People head off to their *pueblos* where their grannies grew up and bump up the numbers, making the local festivities worthwhile.

It was a return to the simple life; burning wooden figures, chasing greased up animals and throwing vegetables at each other.

We'd always closed the shop for a period of time in August. When we were little we'd spend the whole summer in our *pueblo* and still we'd sob our eyes out each time we had to go back to London.

It was the days before easyJet and we'd have come through France, our car so overloaded that my brother and I would be sharing the backseat with a load of luggage. He'd stretch his legs over the bags and fall asleep with his head on my lap and I'd be squashed up against the window, staring out at the endless fields, savouring the beat of the Gypsy Kings.

It was comfortable enough until we arrived in the Pyrenees and then the bags would start falling on top of us as Papa sped around those mountain roads he knew so well.

Sometimes we'd have to stop so I could throw up bread sticks.

When that happened Mum would let me sit in the front seat.

I delayed a visit to my *pueblo* this time and went to Barcelona beach instead.

I wouldn't normally have gone to the city's beach but it was too late in the day to head to one further away.

Turned out Barcelona beach is not a well-kept secret.

It was littered with bodies stripped to the bare minimum. Flesh lolling side by side, sweating, burning and wobbling.

'*Está carbonizado!*' Cookie chuckled, nodding at a bloke who had successfully barbequed himself, and was now a deep shade of lobster.

The moment my foot touched the beach I had a bad feeling. The sand had the colour and texture of road grit.

We were squeezed in between a yellowing sun bed and a couple of cremating Australians. I spread out a newly-purchased towel which proudly said, 'Tenerife!'

The smell of vomit wafted over.

'It's baby poo,' my brother said, although how he knew I didn't know.

I rubbed sun cream over my face in an attempt to neutralise the smell.

Out at sea, rubbish bobbed on the waves. I'd thought to go for a swim but there was no way I was going in there.

I lay back and tried to relax.

'*Agua! Fanta! Cerveza! Bieeere!*' someone shouted nearby. And then another voice echoed the call further away.

I closed my eyes. *No pasa nada* . . . at least I'd get a tan.

'*Coco! Coco!*' another voice cried.

'*Agua! Cerveza! Coca Cola!*'

Other people didn't seem to know what they were selling and cried out something unintelligible.

'*Nano nano nana!*' they called, '*nano nano!*'

Nano? Did you eat it or drink it? Maybe you wore it.

I could've born the racket if it hadn't stunk so much.

I'm deeply affected by smell. I've given up trying to give up sniffing my sleeve. It makes me relax.

If my pillow doesn't smell good, I can't sleep.

My favourite smells are blown out candles, freshly-cut grass, clothes that have dried in the sun, pine trees and coffee. Common favourites I know. But I don't sniff weird things; I just like breathing in good smells.

Smells remind me to breathe.

A man could seduce me with his aftershave alone. Baby poo, on the other hand, doesn't do it for me.

'*Ma-sa-he! Ma-sa-he! Ma-saahge!*' shrieked a woman with a Chinese accent.

An Indian man, in a V-neck jumper and black brogues, walked past with a metal tray.

'*Samosa! Samosa!*'

It was depressing. I was effectively lying in the middle of a market place in just my underwear. I thought I was getting away from the business of buying and selling, but it was everywhere and it was making me feel bad because these sellers all looked so hot and tired.

I was full of nagging questions. How much money could you possibly make from selling samosas? Did they pool their money together? Was it better than the life they had before they arrived in Spain? Were they disappointed? Did they feel envy looking at people on holiday?

I wrestled with these thoughts until it was time to go.

I didn't go back to Barcelona beach. The next day I headed out further to where I used to go to school. The sand was yellow and soft to touch. Last night's storm had filled the sea with red algae. When I came out of the water I smelled of fried sardines.

A solitary black man walked passed selling beads. He smiled at me, his teeth shiny white. I smiled back and inwardly wished him good luck.

For him it needed to be good. It was August.

A weekend sometime in August

Rosie came to Barcelona for my last weekend. We stayed in my brother's girlfriend's flat in the centre of town.

Usually we stay in my parents' house outside the city. Their house is on a built up hill inhabited by guard dogs. Everyone's got one except us.

One move and the hill is barking.

A bus passes by every hour or so. The time-table seems to be someone's rough guess; someone who doesn't take the bus.

I've spent many a time wondering whether I should risk running back up the hill to get the sunglasses or extra cardigan I've forgotten in my rush to get the bus that might or might not have passed a long time ago.

Being in the centre, I fall in love with Barcelona again.

Rosie falls in love with Barcelona too.

Why didn't we live there? We asked ourselves. Why didn't we just come over and do something different.

'Maybe I don't have to look for another job as a researcher,' Rosie gushed, as we wandered along the pier. 'I could do a bar job.'

Rosie is too clumsy to work in a bar but I didn't say anything.

That night we sat on our balcony in shorts and T-shirts and watched people having dinner in the busy square below.

It made sense.

This is what I wanted, to live in a country where I could sit outside and write most of the year.

I just wanted a terrace; a sunny terrace with white walls and terracotta pots full of red geraniums.

I'd be happy with a tiny flat if I had a terrace.

I'd have coffee on my terrace and lunch and dinner.

It would be part-covered and I'd sit out there during the storms at night when the air smelt of earth.

I suddenly wanted to wear white linen and wooden beads and scribble away in a leather notebook.

On Sunday we had lunch near the port.

We ordered paella and a bottle of red wine.

'To living in Barcelona by next October,' Rosie said, holding up her glass.

'Yes,' I said.

But even as our glasses clinked I knew I couldn't make that promise. I was thinking about the book I was trying to write and how I'd a much better chance of succeeding in London.

It wasn't just my writing though.

In that moment I thought of the Date.

I thought, if I fell in love, I wouldn't take off to another country. I would stay wherever it was and enjoy it.

And it wouldn't feel like I was being tied down. It would feel like my world was ballooning.

Soppy?

Of course I felt soppy. I'd had a big glass of wine.

But if we were right for each other, surely we'd end up on a sunny terrace with white walls and terracotta pots full of geraniums *together*, because we'd share the same dreams.

Wednesday 27th August

I'M BACK IN LONDON, back in the shop.

I've got the holiday blues.

Why blues? Why not greys?

Or holiday browns? All right, the latter doesn't have a great ring to it. It sounds like what you get after eating a bit of raw chicken on a night coach while travelling through Peru.

Ah, Peru.

You see, I shouldn't go away because every time I do, I get an idea.

Not a useful idea, like the plot for my novel or a way to sell chandeliers in bulk. But ideas which are inevitably unfulfilled and therefore leave me frustrated.

After two weeks in Peru, I thought I'd got it.

'I'll become a volunteer in an orphanage in the Andes!'

I poked about on the internet, ordered some brochures, got demoralised by the price of volunteering, felt anxious for a couple of weeks, then the idea left.

I went to Egypt.

'I've got it!' I thought, 'I'll move to Cairo and study Arabic!'

As I forgot about the handsome animator at the hotel that idea also withered and died.

Next it was me and Rosie on our walk to Santiago de Compostela. We clocked up 350 kilometres in two weeks along the old pilgrim route.

We loved it so much.

'I'll set up my own hostel for pilgrims!' I thought.

But that wasn't to be either. I realised I'd feel envious every time the pilgrims went on their journey and I was left to clear up.

So now it's Barcelona . . . much more accessible than Peru and Egypt as far as I'm concerned, which makes me very concerned. It means I've no excuse now.

I'm anxious. I'm evaluating my whole life.

My bank balance is as balanced as a pregnant cow sharing a seesaw with a nit.

I still haven't transformed the shop into Harrods.

While I was turning my life into a spider diagram, the moody woman from the newsagent came into my shop.

'You have to sign something for me,' she said.

My head was already shaking. Unless it was for her own arrest I wasn't signing anything. She's the moodiest woman on the street and refused to pay us for a job we'd done, that is, until my mum went in with her Celtic blood bubbling and told her husband to *please* hand it over or she'd clobber them both with a sheep.

Well, something like that.

The newsagent woman wanted me to sign a petition against the Dress Shop Man and his new shop.

'He's made me move my newspaper box in front of my shop!'

Whose shop should it be in front of then?

I like the Dress Shop Man. I like the dresses in the Dress Shop Man's shop.

'I can't,' I told her, 'I get on with him. I'd feel like I was stabbing him in the back.'

She was enraged.

'He spit on me!' she cried. 'I called the police!'

I'd have spat on her too if I'd been able to muster enough enthusiasm. But I couldn't because I had the holiday blues.

She told me I knew nothing about nothing.

The Dress Shop Man came in after she'd left and told me *his* version of the story.

It sounded like the newsagent woman needed a better idea.

Damn. I could've given her one of mine.

Sunday 31st August

I'VE ADDED SITEMETER TO my blog. It counts how many people are reading it.

Today, I've had two hits.

I'm concerned those two hits are me checking if anyone's read it.

September

Wednesday 3rd September

I'VE NEVER HAD A song.

I mean, I've never had a song *with* someone.

Like a romantic reminder of a special moment.

I can't remember any music the night I met the Date. I only remember the football chants and screaming the goal keeper's name with a girl from San Sebastian:

'Ca-si-llas! Ca-si-llas! Ca-si-llas!'

What were the chances of us meeting? It still amazes me.

I only went to North London to meet other Spanish supporters who last minute moved to a different pub altogether. If I'd decided to watch the match somewhere nearer me, or if Papa had decided to come and watch with me, or if Spain, and this is the most important factor, if Spain had lost, then I would never have met him.

And if *he* hadn't gone to meet some Spanish girl at the bar to see the match, because the truth has come out, some Spanish girl that never showed up thank the Lord, then he wouldn't have been there to meet me either.

The other thing that amazes me is that after all my Friday nights dancing salsa and meeting Colombians, the Colombian I meet is in a sports bar in North London and doesn't like salsa.

I don't mind that he doesn't come dancing with me.

In fact I don't think dates and salsa mix very well because Latin clubs are generally so full of testosterone you could grow a beard just walking up to the bar.

It's fun just to go with Rosie. And I love the freedom of dancing with different people. If the Date came, I might only be able to dance with the Date.

Having said that, recently I've caught myself thinking that he's the only person I really want to dance with.

That's why I brought it up when he rang me at the shop.

I suggested he came out one Friday.

'I want to try other types of dancing,' he said.

'I'm up for that,' I said, thinking how bonding it would be.

'My friend has asked me to go to a swing class with her.'

I felt winded.

'It'll be fun,' he said.

I just blurted it out. 'You can't go dancing with another girl!'

He laughed.

'I'm serious,' I said, 'It's not fair!'

He thought I was being funny.

But my mind went on overdrive.

In seconds I could see how it would pan out.

Dancing was all contact. It was smiles and hands and swinging hips.

Yes, it would start as one innocent class between friends. But next they'd be having a coffee after class, from the coffee would come the date, the date between 'just good friends' which would end in an accidental kiss as they both reached down to pick up a dance shoe that she'd purposefully dropped.

And after the kiss, it would spiral out of control.

By class six they'd be boyfriend and girlfriend, as good as married.

It felt horrible.

Tragic.

I'd met someone who loved to dance and he didn't want to dance with me.

I tried to sound normal on the phone. I tried to laugh it off, but I was thinking we should break up now to save more heart break in the future.

I controlled myself though.

I didn't fall quiet like I'm prone to do when I don't like something. I suppose I knew I was being ridiculous and I didn't want to push him away.

Thursday 4th September

WHAT A PARANOID PRAT I am.

I'm writing a short story about my reaction to the swing class.

I'm calling it 'Camouflage.' Not the best title but if I spend too much time thinking about titles then I don't do any writing.

It's about how your mind can take you for a ride, how you let yourself believe stupid things.

I need to write as much as I can and promote myself.

I won't always have a job like this, which doesn't make me anxious.

It used to make me anxious because I used to spend all day thinking I should be somewhere else. But I'm starting to realise you can only be where you are and that's why I'm writing a blog about where I am. When I move then I'll write about something else.

The Date set up a group page for my blog on Facebook.

'Write a sentence or two about it,' he said, and passed me his laptop.

'What, right now?'

I was worried I'd write something rubbish.

'Yes, do it.'

It probably would've taken me hours if I'd been on my own.

That's what good about the Date; he's a doer, he makes things happen. He's not someone you break up with over something silly, like going to a swing class with his friend.

Saturday 6th September

CUSTOMERS ASK HOW LONG we've had the shop.

'Ages,' I say. 'I was born in a box out the back.'

Sometimes they think I'm being serious.

'Crikey,' they say, eyeing the hazardous backroom with its dangling cables and suspended metal hooks.

My parents had the shop before I was even born. As teenagers, my brother and I used to work on Saturdays assembling light fittings and stringing crystal.

We'd attach cable to a tiny chain and push the chain through the brass arms of the fittings.

We'd tighten the arms on with a nut and a 13ml spanner. Mum would check we'd put the connectors on tight. That was my worst bit. My brother was better with the pliers than me. My connectors were always falling off.

I knew I'd become an adult the first day I was left in the shop by myself. I was nineteen and didn't look like one. People kept asking me where 'mummy' was and if I was enjoying my School Holidays. Customers still comment on how I've grown. They ask me if I'm studying, if I'm getting married, if I have children, if I'll take over the business and sometimes, if we sell fridges.

My parents never intended to have a shop. I'm not sure what they intended to do.

At some point my Mum and Rosie's Mum sold ladies' boots.

Rosie found a pile of them in her Mum's loft: lovely, soft, Spanish boots in black and red leather.

They were twenty-five years old and the same shape and style as the boots on the high street. We kept two pairs each and wore them and wore them until one day the cobblers shook their head and said there was no more they could do.

My parents have been talking about closing the shop for years.

In primary school I told everyone we were closing up and moving to Spain. People stopped believing me when I was still saying it five shoe sizes later.

We did move in the end. At least Papa did, and then my brother and then me. And yes, I did come back. But what matters is that I went, because sooner or later, if you want it enough, things *do* happen.

Today, as I watched Mum press the sponge tip of the shoe whitener against the shop window, I felt knots in my stomach. I didn't take my eyes off the letters forming. This was history. I'd remember this forever.

She tidied it up, wiping away the white streaks before stepping down from the ladder.

It wasn't a very big sign; a whisper rather than a shout.

CLOSING

I couldn't believe we'd finally written it. I felt strange.

It was like putting down a family pet. It wasn't a very fun pet. It was a bit of a wild pet; the type you couldn't play with or stroke. Like a stick insect. But it was a stick insect that you'd had so long that even though it was a bit rubbish you still felt sad it had died.

A woman popped her head around the door while we were staring at it.

'You closing down?'

Mum started to mumble something vague.

'Yes,' I said. It was time to accept it.

Her eyes lit up.

It was horrible.

'Oooh, I'll be in later then!'

She said it as if we'd announced a party.

Vulture!

We worked until late. It was painful to slash prices. Our South East London and African customers are such shrewd bargainers we have to be careful not to end up paying them to take a light away.

To give ourselves a boost, we opened a bottle of white wine. It was warm because I hadn't thought to get one from the fridge.

After a while I noticed the knots in my stomach had gone.

I know big changes don't happen overnight, but I think I'm ready.

Sunday 7th September

I SPENT THREE YEARS writing a novel called *Painting Pears*. It was about a procrastinating painter who worked, surprisingly enough, in a light shop.

For three years people kept asking me if I'd finished it. It started to feel a bit of a joke.

I did finish it though.

In fact, I finished it three times.

When I got back from South America I read it through. I knew almost immediately that the book wasn't going to work. It was like that moment of clarity when you know your relationship with someone is over. The relief outweighs the sadness because finally you're free to embark on something new.

It wasn't a waste of time. It was my training. Like past relationships, they're only a waste of time if you can't learn from them, if you can't grow because of them.

So now I'm writing this new book.

And it will be better than *Painting Pears* because I'm older now and not as angry.

The main character is a phoenix. I'm trying to piece it together.

I sat with the Date in Primrose Hill and talked about it.

We'd bought olives, brie and crackers from a nearby deli.

The sun came out for a while.

Wednesday 10th September

'BUT WHY DON'T YOU write your novel at the shop?' Seb said.

He's the third friend to ask me that this month.

I was up a ladder trying to hang up a five-arm light fitting onto some moving chain. My arm was throbbing and I thought if I missed the hook one more time, I would drop the damn thing.

'Because I'm working!' I cried. 'You know, I do actually *do* work in the shop.'

'I'm not suggesting you sit on your arse all day doing nothing,' he said, then trailed off. 'Well, I suppose I am.'

I feel I need to dispel a myth about being a shop assistant, that I don't spend my day perched on a stool filing my nails. In fact, my nails are rubbish.

That's one thing on my agenda when I leave the shop. I'm going to get long, fake nails with bright patterns and a stick-on diamante. They'll be so long that I'll have to use a Dictaphone to record my book and get someone else to type it up.

Until that time of course, I'll continue sacrificing my hands for the cause, although sometimes I just want to slap somebody with them.

Like Belle.

What a bossy woman.

She came in, panting.

'I ran off the bus when I saw the closing sign!' she cried. 'Why are you closing? You can't! I need my crystals! I need two small chandeliers!'

We've a lot of gold bling going for peanuts but she wanted silver. Silver is mostly new stock which we aren't in a hurry to clear.

'I could probably make you something for next week,' I said.

'You must have two of *something* to take away!' she wailed.

'This isn't Argos. It's not mass produced,' I told her and then as an after-thought, 'which is probably why we're closing down.'

I rustled up a chandelier frame from the backroom.

'I need two.'

'Two will take time.'

'I can talk to you while you do it.'

I wanted to hit her over the head with the frame.

'I have to string the crystal too,' I said.

'I'll help you.'

'Can't you just come back?'

But she wasn't going anywhere.

Another customer came in and decided on a light.

It was the only light without a ceiling plate. The ceiling plate is the metal dish at the end of the chain that sits flat against the ceiling.

If it'd been silver or gold, I would've borrowed one off another fitting, but it wasn't either. It was a brownish black colour with gold brushstrokes.

He said he'd come back in ten minutes.

I went back to making Belle's chandelier.

It was going to take ages.

I needed to attach three metal tiers together by small strings of chain. The loops of the chain weren't at all malleable and the skin on my fingers was blistering against the handle of the pliers.

I had to have the same amount of loops connecting the different tiers so the light would hang straight. But I kept miscounting and having to do it over again and each time it hurt my fingers even more.

It didn't help that Belle kept interrupting me with price queries.

'How much is that candle stick?'

'Uh . . . I think it's . . .'

'The big one not the small one.'

'30?'

'What about the small one?'

And I was feeling increasingly panicked about the missing ceiling plate. I didn't know where I'd find one; the only way out would be to paint one and that was a job for Mum, the artist, who was back in Spain again.

While I was experiencing this inner turmoil a little old lady came in to buy a picture frame.

'Will you put it in for me dear?' she said, holding up a school photo that was far too large for the frame she'd chosen.

'I'll have to cut off one of the kids,' I told her.

'That's alright dear.'

I swept my tools to one side and got out the Stanley knife.

'Which one?'

'Oh you choose, dear. I don't think they're my grandson's friends.'

I sliced off a chubby boy's arm.

The man appeared to collect his light and found I'd done nothing to it. I threw it in a plastic bag, gave him some freebie light bulbs and promised to send him the ceiling plate as soon as I could.

Then I turned to Belle and told her she'd have to come back.

'Alright, I'll be here at six,' she said reluctantly.

The mini chandeliers took me four hours to make. She didn't come back at six.

'Oh sorry,' she said, when I rung her. 'I'll come in next week .'

My hands were sore. My nails were dreaming of sparkly nail varnish.

I took the long way home, distributing our cards which we'd written *Closing Down* over in red felt tip.

And that's pretty much why I don't write my book at the shop.

Saturday 13th September

ROSIE AND I WENT to a salsa event in Brixton last night. Except it wasn't salsa at all.

It was Vallenato, some kind of Colombian folk music.

There was a band of ten on stage and it looked like they were a mix of nationalities.

There wasn't much dancing, just swaying and singing along.

I felt awkward. I bought a drink just so I could hold something.

Rosie started chatting to a clean shaven young Colombian, called Alejandro.

'How old is he?' I asked.

'He won't tell me,' she said.

They had a dance while I got stuck with some weird guy who liked to wear leather on a Wednesday.

They exchanged numbers.

I texted the Date.

We went home.

I felt restless because I'd really felt like dancing my heart out. I used to go to salsa every Friday but now I've got other commitments.

Like the blog.

I checked my Facebook group.

44 members.

That cheered me up.

I haven't missed a week so far. I'm not getting any quicker at writing them but it all feels worthwhile when people leave positive comments.

Monday 15th September

TODAY IT FINALLY FELT like the Closing Sale was having an impact.

People were hungry to buy and of course they all came in at the same time.

I was on my own, juggling five customers, rotating my apologies every time I left one.

Goods were flying out the door.

I was dishing out deals, packing up picture frames, handing out light bulbs and keeping my eye on the toddler who was racing a red car around the shop.

A quiet French man chewed on his lips as he considered the ceiling plate of a chandelier.

'*Mais oui!*' cried his indignant wife, tossing aside the instruction pamphlet. 'I can do this myself.'

I wanted to shake her hand. That's the type of customer you want; no nonsense, up for a challenge.

'How about the matching floor lamp?' I suggested

They couldn't resist.

The toddler's mother bought a green glitter lamp.

I sold a pile of frames from the window display.

Jim, a regular, bought the last dimmable up-lighter.

It was only eleven thirty. Bring it on London!

And there was still the well-spoken woman who smelt of eau d'ashtray and her daughter with the big teeth.

'Your first flat is always very difficult,' the mother said, explaining their indecision.

I can't imagine ever owning a flat so I didn't feel very sympathetic. But I played my part with a smile and switched on all the lamps they wanted to see before leaving them to deliberate.

I served another customer; a customer who was more interested in the original prices than the sale prices.

'But how much *was* it?' she kept asking.

In the end she bought a thirty pound spotlight because the well-spoken woman said she'd seen the same one elsewhere for a hundred and fifty. The spotlights weren't even reduced but as she seemed to think she'd already got a bargain I didn't bother with a discount.

Finally the woman and her daughter settled on a weighty antique floor lamp. Thankfully, they were very tentative barterers and the price was good for everyone.

At the end of the day I was in high spirits. I opened a bottle of red wine and danced around the kitchen to Santana and *The Motorcycle Diaries* soundtrack.

Then I worked on my short story until the wine made me too sleepy to concentrate.

Tuesday 16th September

DIVERSITY IS THE SPICE of life. And this job is riddled with it.

A text message from Mum in Spain woke me up at 9.59, not ideal when you open a shop at ten.

The rushing began.

I was open forty minutes late.

I found I'd missed a delivery.

Jim brought back his dimmable up-lighter.

'It's buzzing,' he said.

I made tea and the milk was off.

I tipped a box of pins all over the floor.

The posh lady came back with the antique lamp.

'She was almost in tears,' she said, about her daughter, 'but it really did-n't work in the room.'

The refund was painful and I grimaced when she asked me how the Sale was going.

I imagined everyone we'd ever sold to stampeding into the shop and clamouring for refunds. I thought about going upstairs to the office and not coming down. They couldn't have their money back if I wasn't there.

At the end of the day an Irish lady bought an expensive gold floor lamp.

'I'll be so sad to see you go,' she said. 'We'll all miss this shop. It brings a bit of class to the road.'

I gave her a free light bulb.

Sunday 21st September

I FINISHED MY 'CAMOUFLAGE' story and sent it off to Tales of the Decongested, an event set up to promote short stories.

If it's accepted I get to read it out in Foyles Book Shop in Charing Cross.

I'm not hopeful. But I need a lift. I need a mini success to keep me believing that this writing dream is possible.

Sometimes I feel a wave of tiredness.

I feel I'm treading water, that I've been treading water for hours.

I worry that one day I'll give up.

That I'll stop and I'll sink.

I also worry that if I don't stop I'll just keep on treading water, nothing more.

I burst into tears while I was with my date. I suppose it'd been building up.

'What if nothing ever happens?'

'It will darr-ling,' he said, hugging me. 'Just keep going.'

Thursday 25th September

WE DIDN'T PUT CLOSING down on the shop window, just Closing.

I suppose we were feeling a little over-sensitive that day and Closing *down* sounded too negative.

Closing *down* sounded like we were giving up instead of choosing our own destiny. Because I like to think we're choosing our destiny and it's not choosing itself. At least I like to think we influence it.

Anyway, our sign is causing problems.

People don't get it.

'You're closing?' customers ask.

'Yes.'

'But you'll still have the shop.'

I meet their gaze and frown a little.

'No. We're closing the shop.'

'Yeah . . . but you'll still be here, right?'

'No.'

Then *they* frown.

'Oh.'

It's starting to get on my nerves. I told Mum it was time to go the whole brutal way and write DOWN.

No one was taking us seriously.

The Dress Shop man came in and perched on the stool by the counter. He asked us how the Sale was going.

'Oh, up and down,' Mum said, 'up and down.'

He leant forward, 'One of my customers said you're always closing down.'

Mum and I looked at each other in disbelief.

We'd had Sale signs up before, and yes there had been that 'End of Lease' one a few years ago, but there'd never been one as dramatic as this.

'That's not fair,' I said. 'We've never closed down before.'

Right, that was it. I'd had enough.

We had to write CLOSING DOWN in big block letters. We were not going to become one of those forever closing down shops.

They'd be sorry.

When we finally disappeared off the street, they'd look up at their bare bulb, hanging in the middle of the room like a single goat's testicle and they'd regret not taking us seriously.

The Dress Shop Man left and an American couple came in with real silver screen drawls.

They called each other honey. They called me by my name.

'I want this one, honey!' the woman said.

'Well, hang on, honey,' her husband said, getting a little agitated. 'Emily is going to show us all the lamps.'

Emily, that's me, invested quite a bit of time showing them their best options. I knew what I was talking about because I'd been doing this for a while. We were specialists. I was a specialist sales assistant. I was someone who knew what they were talking about. It'd taken me a few jobs and a trip round South America to realise that being a sales assistant wasn't so bad after all.

The male Honey came up to the counter with his credit card because he knew I knew what he wanted.

'So Emily,' he drawled, 'Do you have a job?'

I froze, his card suspended above the PDQ machine.

I blinked at him, expecting it to make sense.

Did he think I was another customer?

Did he think I was volunteering?

'Uh . . .' I replied. 'I'm here, aren't I?'

It further confirmed my belief that no one took me or the shop seriously.

Mum overheard.

'She also writes,' she said.

I squirmed.

Yes, I'd reached the 50 members mark on my Facebook blog page, but I didn't think that earned me the title of 'writer.'

'You must have a rich mother to be able to write,' he said.

My mother and I were side by side packing up his dusty, dented lamp. Our fingers were not dripping in diamonds. We let it pass. He talked about himself.

'We got bored of Atlanta,' he said. 'We'd been there ten years.'
He paused.

'But I shouldn't be saying that when you've been stuck *here* all that time.'

Mum's instinct was to tell him how great her life really was. That she spent her time between London and Barcelona and loved it.

When they'd gone I could see she was irritated.

'You take it all with you wherever you go,' she said, '*that's* what I should've said . . . If you're stuck in your head in Atlanta you'll be stuck in your head in London.'

And then this skinny bloke in a blue chequered shirt strolled in.

'You closing down?' he asked.

'Yes.'

'But you'll keep the shop, yeah?'

Next week we'll get the paint out.

Ambiguity is overrated.

Friday 26th September

ROSIE AND ALEJANDRO MET up for coffee.

'Well?'

'It was nice.'

'Go on.'

'He was very gentlemanly. I felt like a girl.'

'Right.'

I was unconvinced.

'No, it was nice.'

'Come on, what was he like?'

'Well,' she hesitated. 'I don't think he quite got my humour.'

'Ah.'

'But it was nice.'

My English teacher banned the word 'nice'. He said it was a nothing word.

'Will you see him again?'

'Yes . . . I think so.'

October

⚜

Thursday 2nd October

PEOPLE HAVE ALWAYS ENCOURAGED me to leave the shop.

'Do something you love,' they say, 'get a job in a newspaper.'

But I don't want to be a journalist. I want to write novels.

It's not just that. After the estate agent's I can't face the thought of working for someone who doesn't care. At least in the family business, my emotional welfare matters.

If I'm about to crack, I know Papa will make a few notes in his diary and find a way of giving me time off.

It was Papa who suggested going to the *pueblo* to look for mushrooms in the mountains. In autumn, that's what people do there. They head off into the bushes with their plastic bags and baskets.

They're secretive about where exactly they go and every year they complain there are no mushrooms because it hasn't rained enough or that it's rained too much so all the mushrooms are rotten.

Papa was surprised when I said yes. I think he thought I'd want to stay in London to see the Date. Not that I've talked to him much about him.

My dad's too wise for that. He's seen it all before.

Apart from my holiday in August I've seen the Date nearly every week since Spain won the Euro Cup. That doesn't mean I'm going to stay in one place waiting to see him.

I thought it would be good to get away, to head into the forest and look for mushrooms.

'Magic mushrooms?' asked every single person I knew.

'No. Real mushrooms . . . *Rovellons* actually.'

'I bet they have them in Borough market,' Velvet said.

'It's not the same.'

My date teased me about it.

Meat might be the way to his heart so I promised to bring him back a local sausage.

It was just me and my Dad on the trip. Mum stayed to run the shop.

We arrived in the village at night; the air smelt of earth and blown out candles.

This was the village of my childhood. It was where I'd learnt that lizards lost their tails when in danger and a *Calimocho* was wine mixed with Coca Cola.

In the morning the sun was shining.

Time expanded.

Old men sat on benches chewing toothpicks. They grunted and stared. Everyone who passed by was under scrutiny.

Papa and I sat out on the balcony with our books, pens and newspapers.

CRASH!

The Spanish papers had adopted a tabloid tone for that week's disaster. The stock exchange was collapsing; the banks were in trouble.

Papa rubbed his hands together and looked excited.

'I'm getting very worried!' he said.

I looked across at the sleepy plaza.

The sun was out and a breeze was gently lifting the pants on the washing line.

I could hear the clang of cow bells.

It was hard to muster any worry in the *pueblo*.

Perhaps If I'd had money I would've been a bit more concerned. It felt good not to own anything.

In the afternoon we headed into the forest.

I felt about twelve years old with my wicker basket and as free as a mountain goat.

Rovellons are like big, fat orange buttons sown into the earth.

There weren't lots about and I was thrilled by each one I found.

'We're going back to our roots, aren't we?' I said. 'We're hunters again!'

In the evening, Papa fried the mushrooms with garlic.

'What else could we find in the forest?'

I had a devilish desire to shoot a rabbit.

'Cauliflower,' Papa said.

We followed the same simple pattern each day.

I wrote endlessly, plotting my novel about the phoenix until my head hurt.

It was perfect.

Sunday 5th October

OUTSIDE THE VILLAGE, EVERYTHING got complicated again.

As promised, I bought a local cured sausage. But then I wondered if I could take it on the plane.

'*Papel de plata*,' Papa said, handing me tin foil to wrap it up with.

Later I got a text from my mum.

'Whatever you do, don't put the sausage in tin foil. It comes out black on the X-ray.'

I imagined walking through security armed with my silver-coated sausage. I waved it around like a Jedi in front of the guards but they couldn't see it.

'Wrap it in the shape of a gun,' my brother scoffed.

Taking a pair of tweezers *and* a sausage in my hand luggage was too risky.

I left the tweezers.

In the airport I watched the premature queue forming in front of the gate which had yet to open. I was in group A but I wasn't going to move from my seat until the last minute. What was there to gain from getting into a queue half an hour early?

Fools! I thought. There's space for everyone! The plane isn't going without you!

And then I caught myself. I was sounding like a grumpy old man; all I needed was a toothpick.

Anyway, some of the people in the queue were smiling.

I tried to relax. I could smell the city.

Time shrank.

A man sat down beside me and I felt a sense of comradeship because he was shunning the queue too. But then I saw his boarding pass was in a smart plastic folder and I knew we weren't comrades after all. Somewhere in the dark belly of my bag, my boarding pass was lying crumpled.

Monday 6th October

THE DATE WAS HAPPY with his cured sausage. I don't know if his flat mate will be though when the smell creeps through the three plastic carrier bags I've wrapped it in.

Thursday 10th October

I DID IT. I sent one of those text messages.

Why is there always coverage when you send one of *those* text messages? Why do you always have battery? Why isn't there a preventative pop up window like there is whenever you do something on the computer?

Are you certain you want to send this potentially humiliating message?

Yes, yes, I'm sure.

Another pop up window.

Are you really sure you want to send it? I'm sensing soppy signals.

Yes, I know what I feel, I'm cool with it.

The third pop up window.

Are you really, really sure you want to send it, even though when you don't get a reply you're going to have that horrible sinking feeling that you've come across as a needy, love-struck idiot?

Yup.

Message Sent.

A few moments passed.

I got that horrible sinking feeling I'd come across as a needy, love-struck idiot.

No reply.

Pop up window.

I did warn you.

I deleted every text message I'd ever drafted, re-drafted, sent and received.

It never happened, okay. I was still cool.

Doubt spread like a rash. My stomach muscles tightened.

Tighter, tighter, tighter.

I felt like I'd swallowed an ironing board.

I could hear Mum's voice whispering across from Spain where she'd just landed.

'Get your attention on something! Do something practical!'

I got a duster and dragged out the Hoover.

I rearranged the picture frames. I washed a crystal table lamp.

In the door way, a customer clicked his teeth at me and beckoned me with his finger.

Idiot.

He bartered over a four pound picture frame.

'Three pounds and we do business,' he said.

'Four quid. Take it or leave it.'

I felt tired of everyone. I was going into hiding to write my novel.

I checked my mobile.

I was so over this *feeling* rubbish.

I checked my mobile again.

Sooo over it.

And off it went, the commentary: I'd learn to drive, move to the mountains, buy a goat, grow tomatoes, have a herb garden . . .

Three days passed like that; three days of feeling like I had a chopping board shoved down my oesophagus.

And then this morning, I went to a funeral.

Only twenty eight years old.

'You're too young to be going to a funeral,' someone said.

Inside the church my heart melted.

Love; it was everywhere.

All encompassing; all-inclusive.

So beautiful, it made me cry.

I realised there was nothing humiliating, nothing embarrassing about loving someone. So why should I keep it a secret?

Friday 10th October

IT WAS VELVET'S BIRTHDAY and the Date couldn't come because he had a job.

'You look amazing,' someone said, which made it feel worse that the Date hadn't come.

'Did he ever reply?' Velvet asked me.

'Nope,' I said, 'But maybe I sent it for the wrong reason.'

I suppose I hadn't quite let the feeling of rejection go and I'd been thinking about my reaction.

'It's all about motivations,' Rosie had said, the last time she'd dropped by the shop.

Perhaps I'd only written that text message to receive a text message.

It wasn't that I loved him so much as I wanted him to tell me he loved me.

Monday 13th October

I'D ONLY JUST GOT into work and was about to sink my teeth into a warm *pain au chocolat*, when a man flung the door open.

'I have a big house with a high ceiling,' he announced. 'What light should I have?'

He jangled his car keys.

'High ceiling, high ceiling . . .' I echoed, trying to rev my brain up. It'd been a late night and I wasn't feeling good. I put my breakfast down. 'Can you give me another clue? A colour?'

He leant out of the door to check for traffic wardens.

'Gold?' I suggested.

'No, not gold!' he cried, turning back. 'Something modern!'

'Right . . . Silver?'

Petra was great at the customer sell when she worked here part-time.

'Ah yes!' She'd say, 'What you want is something dazzling but muted, not too silver, not too gold, something neutral yet tantalising.'

I don't think she ever knew what she was talking about.

'Something organic but with dark undertones,' she'd continue.

'Yes, yes!' the customer would say, nodding their head excitedly.

'Something elegant but edgy . . .'

'Exactly! Art Deco!' and they'd point at the most frilly, decorative piece of bling in the shop. 'Art Deco like that, right?'

My friend would hesitate.

'Well, yes, I suppose . . . Art Deco with a Baroque twist.'

But she wasn't here. It was just me and a man with a high ceiling.

'What about this one?' he cried, pointing at a glass up-lighter. 'Is this modern?'

He didn't wait for an answer before he was onto the next one; this time a wrought iron five light.

He had to touch them all; turning them round, sending them into a spin.

Soon the whole ceiling seemed to be moving.

I hate it when customers do that.

The lights are on runners. If they're pushed to the end of the runner they'll fall off the other end. I know because I've pushed one to the end of the runner before.

'*Only Fools and Horses,*' customers often say, 'You know the one with . . .'

Yes, the one with the chandelier that falls down.

Seen it. Done it.

'What about this?' the man kept asking. 'Is this a good one? Or that one? Or better this one? Is that modern?'

Why didn't he just go for the one he liked?

'You're going to be living with it,' I said. 'Choose one that makes you happy.'

That wasn't what he wanted to hear.

'What about this black one? Do you have it in silver? Is silver the most modern colour you have?'

I needed to switch him off for one second.

'Wait, hang on!'

Then I directed him to the window display and pointed at an elegant Murano chandelier with fluid transparent arms.

'How about this?' I said, with reverence.

His forehead crumpled.

Silence.

Perfect.

At that moment a woman and young man came into the shop. It was obvious they were mother and son. They were both smartly dressed. The man was in a pale pink shirt and cream chinos. I noticed his lovely brown leather shoes.

My customer turned to them.

'Is this modern?' he cried, pointing at the light I'd suggested.

The young man was surprisingly unfazed by being shouted at.

'Well, it's retro.' He glanced at me. 'Isn't it?'

'It's a modern play on classic,' I said.

My school friend would've been proud.

He, on the other hand, wasn't convinced by me or the light.

'Madam! Madam!' he called after the mother. 'What about this one?'

For the next ten minutes he directed all his questions at the mother and I was left hovering redundantly around the counter, looking longingly at my uneaten *pain au chocolat* and wondering where I went wrong.

To my relief Madam responded well to her new sales role.

By the time they'd left the shop there were three fewer light fittings hanging from the ceiling.

Friday 17th October

YESSS!

My story 'Camouflage' has been chosen for a reading at Foyles!

The organiser said it was 'terrific'! I've never used the word 'terrific' in my life! Terrific!

Some credibility at last!

It means they'll put my blog link on their website too.

Connie came in when I'd just received the news so I was really chatty with her.

'You seem different,' she said, 'are you still with that bloke?'

'Which bloke?'

'Oh look at you, you're blushing!'

I turned to the mirror behind the counter and noted my pink cheeks. To be fair, I blush at anything and can't do much about it.

'When did I tell you?'

'The other week. The one from Cameroon.'

'Colombia.'

'That's it.'

I grinned.

'Oh, look, you're all in love.'

'No.'

'What does your dad think?'

'They haven't met.'

'You going to move in with him?'

'No.'

After that we covered topics from gravy to waxing, and I didn't feel compelled to string crystal because I was actually enjoying myself.

Tuesday 21st October

At home everything happens around the kitchen table.

When I imagine having my own family, I always picture them around a kitchen table. I also picture them as Mexican, which I suppose is a bit random, but not as random as the chandeliers we had to make tonight.

We'd had 'a touch', as Alfie calls it.

A sale of three chandeliers, smack in the face of the credit crunch.

The only down side was they were probably the most difficult chandeliers to assemble in the whole shop. They needed thousands of crystal beads all strung in different sizes and lengths. At the end of the strings were different shaped pendants: pointy prisms, pear drops, crinkly almonds and so on.

It was baffling which was why we'd left them to the last minute to make.

At eleven o'clock we finally sat down at the kitchen table, ready to roll.

It would've appealed more if we'd been making an exciting profit. But we'd cut our prices down even lower than normal to prove we were being serious about closing the shop.

Not that customers always appreciate a cheap price.

Some are so afraid of being done that they barter you to death. Often I find myself wishing the light would drop on their heads and precipitate the end. Mum takes it less seriously than me but there are times when even *she* can't take any more.

'That's it, I'm not selling it!' she'll snap. 'I'll buy it myself!'

At least the woman who'd bought these knew she'd got a bargain.

In the back of my mind I always knew we'd end up doing the crystal pinning at home.

It was the kind of job that took mental stamina. It wasn't a light you could dress while chatting to George about the change in the air.

Mum had drawn up a dressing diagram especially for it, a knitting pattern for lights.

It looked like a Picasso sketch he'd forgotten he was drawing.

We laid out the trays of crystal in front of us.

Mum sipped her tea.

'Tea is always milkier at this time of night,' she said.

We turned on the CD player and listened to a transpersonal psychologist.

Well, why not.

An hour passed.

I made more tea. Mum looked over her glasses.

'Do I have to drink that?'

It was still too milky.

At one o'clock we got the giggles.

By two o'clock we were starting to flag.

We persevered because we'd promised the customer we'd have it done and if they didn't collect it we weren't going to get paid the balance. Getting paid the balance is the biggest motivator. That and cups of tea.

Wednesday 22nd October

WE ROLLED OUT OF bed straight into the car with the crystal packed and ready.

We were five minutes late and the window cleaner was waiting outside, staring into space. He needed the shutter up and was acting like we'd left it down on purpose to spite him.

Mum dropped me off and went in search of parking.

'Sorry we're late, we've been really busy,' I said, looking for sympathy.

'So you're making lots of money and getting rich.'

'No . . .'

'Well that's what it means, doesn't it?' he said flatly. 'If you're busy, you must be making lots of money.'

And I thought, if I was so rich, would I be up at three in the morning stringing beads together?

'If we were making so much money,' I said, struggling to stay cool, 'we wouldn't be closing down, would we?'

'Closing down?'

I tapped the sign on the window.

'Oh that,' he said, shrugging. 'You've had that up for ages.'

Which was just NOT true!

I kept my mouth shut until I'd got the shutter up with the help of a passing builder.

Then I left him to clean the windows, as badly as ever, whilst I stomped around the shop hissing in Spanish.

Although my inner balance was restored after a cup of tea and an undisturbed *pain au chocolat*, I know it's only a temporary calm.

Sooner or later Mr Window Cleaner and I are going to have serious words.

Monday 27th October

THE DATE AND I hollowed out pumpkins on the weekend.

He'd already bought them when I arrived at his house.

He's in touch with his inner child! I'd thought excitedly.

A slightly nerdy inner child though. He researched the design for his pumpkin online while I just went straight in and attacked it with the knife.

It was the first pumpkin I'd ever done and I was proud of it.

It's not exactly a family tradition. Gramma gave Mum a swede when she was little.

'It was like carving out a carrot,' Mum said.

I lit the pumpkins and put them in the shop window.

A group of scruffy school kids pressed their faces up against the glass to get a better look; it was the scariest thing to happen all day.

That was, until about 4 o'clock.

I knew the woman. She'd already put a deposit on a big crystal chandelier.

She came in and stared up at it.

It's crystal with silver details.

'Everything in my house is gold,' she said. 'It won't match, will it?'

I didn't want to lose the deposit but this light was definitely not gold.

'I've got gold curtains, gold door handles, a gold mirror . . .' Midas continued.

'Well,' I said. 'In *our* house we've got a bit of everything. We've got gold wall lights, a chrome floor lamp, a bit of antique brass . . .'

'Oh,' she said, nodding. 'That'll be alright then.'

I didn't say our house looked good.

Her husband, who'd been lingering on the door step, stubbed out his cigarette and came in with their pit bull.

'There's not much silver on that,' he said, 'It'll be fine, love.'

The dog disagreed and vomited over the floor.

'Oh, that's not like him,' the woman said, bending down to stroke him. 'Are you alright Tel boy?'

My stomach was convulsing.

I covered my mouth to smother the awful retching noises I was making.

The woman turned to me.

'Have you got a tissue darlin'?'

I couldn't even look in her direction. I ran off, still retching, to get some kitchen roll. She wiped up the orange mess. They must've been feeding him Chicken Tikka.

Then I caught sight of my glowing pumpkin.

It couldn't have, could it?

As soon as they'd gone I got a bucket of water, emptied half a bottle of bleach into it and mopped the whole floor.

Tuesday 29th October

I WOULDN'T HAVE PUT a light bulb in any other vegetable. Perhaps I trusted in the spirit of Halloween; the same spirit who tells you it's alright to open the door to a local hoodie carrying a plastic pitch fork.

After one glowing night in the shop window, I discovered the pumpkins were half-cooked.

The fiercer of the pumpkins had morphed into a toothless old man.

Another night and they'd have been puddles of soup.

I had no choice but to send them to landfill.

I put them in a plastic bag, jumped on the bag and stuffed it in the bin outside.

Halloween would be, as ever, just another normal day.

Veronica, a regular came in wearing orange eye shadow.

'That's an interesting colour,' Mum said.

'Yes, everyone says that. They don't do it anymore.'

Veronica often comes in on a Friday to sell second hand jewellery. She also likes to visit the antique market up the road.

I don't really understand what people get out of buying old broken things that anywhere else they'd expect a refund for. People bring lamps in here for re-wiring.

Vintage, they say.

Yes, vintage Ikea.

She held up a necklace; it looked like a glittery thong.

'It's very you,' she told Mum.

Mum held it tentatively around her neck. It didn't matter if she wanted the thong or not, Veronica had closed in on her and there was no escape. She's like a human headphone the way she presses in so closely to talk to you.

In general, I try my best not to engage. I say 'yes' or 'ah' but I'm always worried if I add to the conversation it will never end, and I can only bear the repetition if I'm pinning crystal.

A familiar couple came in, the type that are always doing up their house and make quick decisions.

I made a move to help them but I couldn't get away from Veronica's voice.

'It was a heart necklace with a green stone in the middle,' she explained to Mum. 'You know, like an emerald but not an emerald, but *like* an emerald. And I thought, do I want a heart necklace? I already have one heart necklace, but then I thought well, if they have little heart earrings to match, you know . . .'

More customers came in.

A woman had parked her car in a loading bay and wanted some picture frames quick. Another couple wanted low energy spotlights.

Mum made no attempt to dash past Veronica and serve them. She stayed behind the counter nodding and saying 'yes' and 'ah'.

I felt angry.

I suddenly found myself thinking about the posh estate agent's where I used to work.

Why couldn't we a bit more like them sometimes? A bit more efficient? A bit more ruthless.

Or was it just common sense?

People wanted to buy things but they couldn't because Veronica needed to chat.

Veronica, a customer who wasn't really a customer at all, because she was the one doing the selling . . .

'Do you think I should've bought it?' Veronica continued. 'Maybe I should've waited, or maybe I should've bought a different shape . . .'

Please STOP.

But she didn't; she was on a roll.

'. . . they had some little silver dogs, you know, like dogs but not quite dogs . . . like wolves.'

The husband and wife I was serving agreed on a small chandelier and I brought it over to the counter to pack up.

Veronica wasn't too happy when Mum switched her attention to the wife, who yesterday had slipped on a half-eaten sandwich in Tesco and now had a stiff neck.

'I bet that really hurt,' Mum said.

'I fell once,' Veronica said.

'I'm all bruised down one side,' the wife said.

Veronica homed in on the wife's neck.

'Oh I was much worse than that.'

The couple didn't stay around long. They winked at me as if to say 'Good Luck' and left us with Veronica still talking about the heart necklace.

Mum is so patient.

Like a saint.

So many people will miss her when we close.

At the end of the day we linked arms and made our way home in the cold and dark.

Mum was wearing her brown puffa jacket, the one that looks like a king size duvet. Her huge blue rucksack only just fits over her arms when she wears it.

I noticed the group of face-painted teenagers standing at the corner preparing to pounce on some unsuspecting passer-by. As far as they were concerned it was Halloween all week.

As we approached Mum suddenly lifted her arms up and ran at them.

'Wooooo!' she cried.

Then she came back, locked her arm in mine and on we walked at our usual fast pace.

I was stunned but the teenagers much more so.

In fact, by the time they'd got over their shock and screamed back, we were a good distance away.

'I just had to!' she giggled. 'They were looking so gormless!'

Mum's like that; a saint but not quite.

Thursday 30th October

MUM MADE ME PRACTISE reading 'Camouflage' in the shop.

She never seems to get fed-up.

'Again,' she said, every time I finished. 'Slower.'

I'm reading it out tomorrow.

A couple of old school friends are coming.

Petra will be there. So will Rosie.

The Date phoned and wanted to know what time I'd be on. He'd got a call about a job on the same day.

'I won't finish until 9,' he said.

'It starts at 7 so you'll miss it.'

'Then I won't do the job.'

'It's fine,' I insisted.

I wasn't annoyed. I really meant it.

'It's only a small thing,' I said. 'Do the job. There'll be other times.'

I was worried he might get bored anyway. It was just me and six others reading their short stories in a book shop.

'No,' he said. 'If it's important to you then it's important to me.'

'Oh,' I said, so surprised I stopped in the middle of the street and someone walked into the back of me.

It was such a lovely thing to say.

'You know you'll meet my parents?'

'Great,' he said. 'I don't get nervous about stuff like that.'

I didn't feel nervous about it either. I was still beaming about the last comment.

But I do normally.

Papa is funny and charming when he meets my girl friends. But he's not so fussed about blokes. He eyes them warily and mumbles so they have no idea what he's saying.

Perhaps it'll be different because they both speak Spanish.

November

❧

Saturday 1st November

I ARRIVED AT FOYLES early.

Rosie and Petra were there already nosing through books.

'I feel very *Sex in the City*!' Rosie said.

We went upstairs to the reading gallery.

'Help yourself to wine,' said the organiser. 'You don't need to pay but I'm afraid your friends do.'

I took a glass and saved some seats at the front row.

I sipped my wine slowly; I wasn't going to muck up by getting tipsy and reading too fast.

Velvet and her boyfriend turned up.

'This is exciting,' Velvet said.

I felt so grateful they'd come.

My date came at the last minute, closely followed by my parents.

They didn't have time to meet before it started although I noticed Papa take a long sideways look at him. I wondered what went through his mind, if he thought he was scruffy because he had longish hair.

I was on third.

When I came to read my leg shook and didn't stop until page four.

I was calm inside though. I was enjoying myself. I'd been writing for so long without an audience; it felt so good to share it.

I heard Mum in my head, 'feel your feet on the floor'.

When people laughed I felt so happy.

I knew I wanted to do this again and again.

The interval came.

Mum turned to my date. He was wearing a jacket that his designer friend had made. Its lining was covered in cartoon tuna fish.

'Those fish are upside down,' she said.

I didn't hear how the conversation proceeded because I had to go to the toilet.

Papa needed to go too.

'So that was him,' he said, when we were out of earshot, 'first impressions, very good.'

'But you haven't spoken to him yet.'

'I don't need to. I know these things.'

And they didn't have a chance to talk after the reading either. We had to get to Bloomsbury bowling club for a birthday party, one of the Date's friends.

I got talking to an actor, a girl from Australia. I was feeling elated so I said I was a writer before I mentioned working in the shop.

'What do you write?' she asked.

I told her about my blog since that was what I wrote most regularly and the last time I'd checked I'd had 68 Facebook members.

'Hang on, I think I've read it . . .'

She'd googled tickets to Spain and my blog had come up.

'I read a few, they were really good.'

I felt so excited.

It felt like a turning point in my career as a writer.

The excitement faded a bit when I discovered someone had nicked my wallet.

Sunday 2nd November

PERHAPS BECAUSE I DROPPED out of university I think there's something I don't know.

I don't know what it is I don't know or if I'll ever know.

At university the other students spoke in tongues. They used words like 'dichotomy' and 'contentious' on a normal day-to-day basis. They could be buying a cucumber in a supermarket or queuing for the loo in a pub.

Those words still won't come out of my mouth.

Not knowing words makes me uncomfortable.

Being *Spanglish* makes the hole of missing words even bigger.

In the shop I get lots of Spanish speakers and there are things I don't know how to say.

For instance, 'you need to tighten it up with an allen key mate'.

How do you say that in Spanish?

I suppose if I hadn't been around the shop so much maybe I wouldn't be able to say that in English either.

Is it Allen or Alan? And more to the point, who is Alan?

Then I feel like a fraud; I'm not *Spanglish* after all. I'm just a Brit who likes chorizo and has a lisp.

I wish it wasn't so important but I can't help it.

When I lost my wallet, I also lost my Spanish ID.

I mourned my lost identity for two hours.

Luckily someone handed it to the bouncer and I felt complete again.

Monday 3rd November

THE DATE BOOKED HIS tickets to Colombia.

He's going for six weeks at Christmas.

'Come for New Year,' he said. But I know I won't.

This week he's working on a documentary with a film crew from Chile.

We went to a pub near his house and waited for them to arrive from the airport.

I had sausages and mash and we played Connect 4. He won three times in a row.

'Okay, now you have to do it quickly,' I said, 'without thinking.'

I won when we played like that.

I don't know what that says about me. That I'm cleverer when I'm not thinking?

Wednesday 5th November

MY SHOP IS LIKE a village shop

We do village things, like chat with the postman and make tea for upset locals.

In the upmarket estate agents where I worked, these things were not tolerated.

I used to exasperate my boss because I was too friendly to the telesales callers. She once sat me down and tried to give me a lesson in being abrupt. The lesson was interrupted by a lost elderly tourist.

'Turn left,' my boss barked, not even looking at him.

'There,' she said, once he'd gone. 'You see how I dealt with that.'

'Wasn't it right?' I mumbled.

'What?'

'You said left. Didn't he need to turn right?'

She looked like she wanted to hit me.

'It doesn't matter if it's left or right! The point is you must block out any interruption!'

It soon dawned on me that life is made of up of so many interruptions and fighting them all day was making me miserable.

I didn't want to feel I could only smile if I was getting paid for it so I handed in my notice and went back to the shop.

The shop isn't nearly as efficient as the estate agents.

We're old school.

We let customers pay off for things and keep count on a hand-written receipt.

Like Mr Roberts. He keeps adding items to his. It gets so messy we have to start a new one.

He came in today.

'Now come on, what do I owe you?' he said.

'I'm not sure anymore.'

'If *you* don't know how am *I* supposed to know?'

'Don't you have your receipt?'

'I don't know but I'm here now.' He took a wodge of cash out of his pocket. 'Come on, what have I got to give you?'

I fumbled through a drawer in search of a carbon copy. We've so many receipt books lying around because customers paying off go back so long.

While I was flicking though the latest ones, another regular customer came in for a halogen bulb.

Mum knew him better than me and jumped up to help him.

She let him in on her low-energy lighting conspiracy theory, for free. It's pretty good but who knows, who knows . . .

'It says sixty,' I said, when I found the copy. 'But then you transferred your wife's deposit.'

'So what is it now?'

'Thirty,' I said, scribbling the amount in.

'But I want another picture frame.'

'So it's forty two.'

'For my cat.'

'What?'

'The picture frame is for my cat.'

'Ah.'

'So, come on, what've I bought.'

I ran my finger down the page.

'A brass bell, a coal skuttle, two picture frames and two wall brackets.'

'Have you counted the other picture frame?'

'Oh, no . . .'

'Start again then.'

Mum's customer was visibly amused by our retail version of 'granny went to market . . .'

'A brass bell, a coal skuttle, THREE picture frames and two wall brackets.'

Mr Roberts frowned.

'Is that all?'

'And you've got the chandelier.'

'I don't have it.'

'I mean I've got it but you've paid for it.'

'So who's got it?'

'I have.'

'Right . . . So, start again, what have I got?'

Mum and her customer were now both silently laughing.

'See him,' Mr Roberts said, nodding in their direction, 'he was miserable before he came in here.'

I'd love to be more efficient but I'm glad I didn't learn that lesson in abruptness.

It wouldn't have had the same effect.

Saturday 8th November

I LOGGED ONTO Facebook this morning to check my blog page and noticed someone had tagged the Date.

They were party pictures and my stomach muscles tightened with dread.

I knew that I wouldn't like them. I told myself it was better not to look.

But I opened them because I was in the shop and it was that or dress a crystal chandelier.

There were photos of him with a girl.

He looked like he was besotted with her; she was laughing and he was just staring at her.

I opened another one. They were both sticking their tongues out, going in to lick a lolly pop she was holding.

I felt sick.

I opened another one and it looked like he was about to kiss her.

Eyes closed; lips forward.

I showed Mum.

'That is not a good photo, is it?'

'No,' she said. 'That's not a good photo.'

My stomach muscles tightened even more. I couldn't eat; I didn't want tea.

I couldn't concentrate on stringing crystal.

I was devastated.

'Cuidado con los Colombianos,' a customer had said, herself Colombian. *'Tienen un gran corazón. Un gran corazón para todas las chicas.'*

(*'Be careful with Colombians. They have a big heart. A big heart for all the girls'*)

And she hadn't been the only one to warn me against Colombian men. Women were always saying it to me.

I'd thought it was an ignorant generalisation but looking at those photos a part of me doubted. Maybe they were right. Maybe it was his culture that made him one massive, potentially unfaithful flirt.

I texted him and to his credit, he replied immediately.

He told me not to worry, that she was the producer's girlfriend and that nothing had happened.

But it didn't make me feel much better.

I felt hurt. I felt that it was all for nothing, that he would soon go to Colombia where he would kiss other girls.

'It's not like I'm perfect,' I said, half to Mum, half to myself.

It was horrible because I liked him.

I thought he was, you know, special.

And the pop up window goes: *Should you really carry on writing when you're going to come out with some cringy, soppy stuff that you'll read later and regret?*

Yes, it's all good.

Don't you think you should wait until you're feeling more emotionally balanced?

No, I know what I feel. I like him.

I like his jokes, his smell. I like running my hands through his hair.

I think you've said enough.

I like his dimples when he smiles.

You haven't even had wine you soppy moron.

I like how he gives me advice and talks about my writing like it matters as much to him as it does to me.

Done?

Yes, for now.

When I got home I found the photos had been taken off.

I managed to concentrate on my novel for a few hours.

It freed me; created a space to see how my emotions had tied me up.

'Crash on with what you want to do,' Mum said, 'then you won't rely on other people for your happiness.'

I realised my happiness boat needed a stronger anchor.

I had to forgive the Date, but I also had to step outside the bubble that had been growing smaller. I had to live for now not what might be.

Saturday — still

It's late.

I'm finding it hard to sleep.

It doesn't help that there's a street light right outside my window.

The thing is, what sickens me most about the pictures is, I know I am the same when I'm drunk. That I'm a flirt, hungry for physical contact; that I want to reach out and be liked by people, that there are moments when I forget about the person I'm supposed to be with.

'I'm not perfect but I try,' he'd said.

And how can I get angry, when I'm the same, not at all perfect but trying to be a better person?

Sunday 9th November

MY NOVEL ABOUT THE phoenix just isn't happening.

I know there's a clever idea in there but I can't get my head round it.

I want to write about every day things and every day people, because I get excited about every day things and every day people.

I suppose that's why I've been able to keep up with my weekly blog.

Wednesday 12th November

I'M NOT A HYPOCHONDRIAC; I just occasionally think I'm dying.

Lately, I've been dying of scurvy.

Scurvy was common among 15th century sailors who didn't have access to oranges.

I must have it because my gums bleed and I haven't had an orange in ages.

When I brush my teeth I look like a Vampire.

I consulted a regular customer about it.

'Oh you can't do anything,' he said, 'all gums bleed.'

I told another and she became really serious.

'That's terrible! You must go for a check up.'

But I can't stand going to the dentists. I'd rather hope for the best.

I thought about going though. I thought about buying mouthwash too and those mini brushes that my dad leaves around the sink.

Then one morning I saw a bloody patch on my pillow.

This was serious.

'Papa, I think I'm dying,' I said.

He pulled me over to the light and looked into my mouth.

'Yes,' he said. 'You have receding gums.'

I was horrified. Half an hour later I'd booked to see the dentist.

It must've been the way I walked in.

'You've got gum disease,' she said, before I'd even opened my mouth.

I felt confused, numb even.

'Open wide,' she said, making no attempt to reassure me.

My mind went on overdrive.

I thought about my date.

Would he give up his trip to stay by my bedside while I fought to save my gums?

He hadn't seen his family in months. It would be so unfair.

And how would Mum survive in the shop on her own? She didn't know where any of the picture frames were and had started ringing me every time someone wanted one.

The dentist began to examine my teeth, calling out my failings in a sharp voice.

'6 missing, amalgam needed, 3, 2, amalgam needed, 4 missing . . .'

How had I done so badly?

It sounded like I was going to need a mouth transplant. Or at least dentures.

'It all looks fine apart from that,' she said, at last.

I was stunned. How could I be fine apart from being diseased?

She said she'd give me a filling and do as much cleaning as the NHS let her for free.

I closed my eyes as she emptied her tool box into my mouth.

At one point I peeked and saw a syringe.

I squeezed my eyes shut again.

Something cold slid across my neck.

'How do you brush your teeth?' she asked.

'Ugh,' I replied, gagging on all the appliances she'd left in my mouth.

'To counteract the disease you need to . . .'

Then she started with the cleaning drill and I froze up.

I couldn't hear a thing.

Ten minutes later I was back in my shop, more than 70 quid worse off, still with gum disease and no idea how to cure it.

I don't know what actually happened.

But at least I'm not dying anymore.

Thursday 13th November

A MAN CAME INTO the shop today looking for a reading lamp.

He was the quiet, polite type.

He didn't take long to decide on a satin chrome gooseneck floor lamp.

'Ah yes, this is a great one,' Mum said cheerfully, and started wrapping up its base in plastic. 'You get a free . . .'

Then she stopped abruptly and blushed. She held up the instructions packet.

'There's a free screw in here,' she finished.

But he'd already guessed what she'd been about to say and had turned pink.

Friday 14th November

AN OLD BOYFRIEND ONCE said to me,

'We are born with two fears: fear of falling and fear of loud noises. The rest,' he said, 'are all learnt.'

There are a lot of things I haven't learnt to fear, like spiders, blisters, flying and odd socks.

There are even more things that I have learnt to fear: gum disease, wet dogs, every horror film ever made, rats, fluffy hair, getting too drunk, failing to write and my birthday.

The last one is a bit silly but I'm an anxious sort of person. I jump each time my mobile rings even when I'm calling myself to find out where it is.

And every year as my birthday creeps nearer, my tummy fills with steel butterflies.

I think I have to prove something. I think I should've published a book by now.

I worry I'll talk too much, drink too much, cry, fall over, start a fight and end up throwing my jewellery down the drain in protest against something or other.

Worse perhaps, I think everyone will forget.

My birthday is on a Saturday. Perfect night, except I said I'd go to my Auntie's party.

'Come!' she said. 'You can celebrate your birthday on Sunday!'

She explained it was a reunion of friends who'd all had an important birthday ending in 0 the same year.

'So, it's not even your real birthday Auntie?'

She looked a bit sheepish, 'Well, no, but . . .'

'Come to my Mum's,' Rosie said. 'Then I'll be able to come to your birthday on Sunday.'

Some people make such a difference to a gathering. Rosie is one of those people.

So I decided to do a Sunday lunch thing where people could come and go.

Problem was choosing a pub.

'Any pub, darr-ling!' the Date said, starting to get exasperated by my indecision. 'As long as it's comfy, has good food and live music, it'll be fine.'

Right.

Easy.

It's London.

But every time I need to organise a party I seem to forget everywhere I've ever been. Where do you go out? That's one of my worst questions; it's up there alongside 'what music do you like'?

I don't know.

A bit of everywhere; a bit of everything.

I set up a birthday event on Facebook.

I wish I hadn't because now I can't stop checking it.

A couple of friends rang to tell me they were coming. But as they didn't reply on the Facebook event, for two days it looked like it was just the Date and me going to my birthday.

Monday 17th November

'I'll come in a cab next week and collect everything,' Mr Roberts had said. 'Don't panic, I'll give you warning.'

I was relying on the warning because Mum had inadvertently sold one of his wall brackets and I hadn't secured a replacement.

Stock taking has never been our forte, which does have some advantages. It's always a nice surprise to discover items you didn't know you had: a box of picture frames for instance, or a sought after light. Not so fun when you oversell something and have to re-order from Spain, which incurs an annoyed customer and an annoying transport bill.

Anyway, it was a Monday morning after a late Sunday night.

I made myself a tea, ignored the flashing of the dying fluorescent tube and settled in front of my laptop.

I thought I had time . . . I wanted to slowly warm into the day.

I switched on. . .

Then Mr Roberts stormed through the door.

I jumped up.

He was on a mission and stinking of booze.

'You haven't come to collect everything, have you?' I squeaked.

'Yes, come on, I told you I was coming.'

A pale-faced man in a flat cap walked in behind him. He was evidently the cabbie.

I felt the panic rising inside.

'You have done those wall brackets, haven't you? Here's what I owe you.'

He started counting out twenty seven pounds on the counter.

'I . . . uh . . . the wall brackets . . . they . . . uh . . . they broke!'

Mr Roberts stopped counting and looked at me.

'The . . . uh . . .' I was struggling to get a grip with my story. Telling fibs to customers isn't what we're about. We usually just confess our short comings, but this time I couldn't. He was standing in front of me like an angry bull. 'The lamp holder was faulty . . . we've sent them back to the factory.'

'Oh come off it!' Mr Roberts spat.

He wasn't the jolly man he was last week. He didn't want to play 'granny went to market'.

'Look,' I pointed to a different wall bracket. 'I could make two of these.'

He looked at them. I knew he wasn't concerned much about the design, he just wanted to complete the action. If he'd been fussy his wall bracket would probably never have been inadvertently sold.

'Alright I'll take them now.'

'But I need to put the crystal on them,' I stammered. 'Mum could drop them in to you.'

'You see this is my mate Danny,' he said, nodding at the man behind him, 'and he's doing me a favour coming down here. I don't want to mess him about.'

Danny, in the flat cap, stared at me with watery blue eyes.

'Give them to me as they are,' Mr Roberts said. Then he leant in, his breath sticky with drink. 'You could come over and put the crystal on for me couldn't you? You'd do that for me, wouldn't you?'

The idea of being alone with him in his flat, drunk as he was . . . it didn't bear thinking about.

Danny sensed as much.

'I think the girl will be happier doing them here,' he said.

He convinced him and carried everything but the bare wall brackets to the car parked outside.

Mr Roberts lingered a little longer.

'If I'm not too drunk later on, I'll ring you to let you know when Danny is coming.'

'Oh,' I said and before I could stop myself, 'are you celebrating something?'

He steadied himself and looked me in the eye.

'I drink every day. I suppose you'd say I'm an alcoholic.'

'Oh.'

'I'm not one of those dirty ones who lie about on benches. I shower every day.'

'No, of course . . .'

'All geniuses are drug addicts or alcoholics. You know why? It's because genius and logic don't go together.'

'Uh yeah . . . Hemingway.'

I'd never read Hemingway but I knew there were a lots of bars named after him. Well, I remember walking passed one in La Habana anyway.

'Genius and logic just don't go,' he insisted. 'That's why. Do you see?'

'Yeah yeah . . .' I said, nodding.

He left me to ponder that thought under the flashing glare of the dying fluorescent tube.

And I came to the conclusion I'd never done anything remotely clever, let alone genius, after a bottle of wine.

Unless I count my sudden ability to speak French.

Which is something, I suppose.

Tuesday 18th November (*every 2–5mins*)

FACEBOOK BIRTHDAY EVENT: 4 people attending, 2 maybe attending

Loads of people away.

Some busy.

Perhaps because it's on a Sunday.

And short notice.

Should I have done it on Saturday and missed my Auntie's party?

Wednesday 19th November (*every 1–3 mins*)

FACEBOOK EVENT: 5 PEOPLE attending, 2 maybe attending

I can't stop checking.
I should've done it on Saturday.
No, Sunday is more relaxed

20th–29th November

THE CHECKING ON FACEBOOK has got out of hand.

If I'm not checking my birthday event then I'm checking my blog group page.

Members: 96, by the way.

I keep changing my status too.

Status: *4 more people until we are 100 members!*

And then I check my group again and find it's gone up by one so I change my status again.

Status: *3 more people until we are 100 members!*

And then someone decides to leave the group and then I change it again.

Status: *4 more people until we are 100 members!*

Then I check my birthday event and worry that it's tomorrow and no one's going to come.

Sunday 30 November

PETRA SENT ME A Happy Birthday message at midnight. She never forgets.

Mum gave me a rust coloured scarf with matching gloves and a hard-back National Geographic notebook, orange with an elastic to keep it shut.

Work was as normal until the afternoon when I got a surprise visit from the local salsa addict. He'd been to see Treasure Island last week.

He brought me a birthday card with a dance shoe on it, a salsa CD and the ingredients to make grog.

It was such a treat.

Rum, cinnamon, lemonade and a dash of lime – the shop counter turned into a bar with old Cuban music playing in the background.

I hadn't been out dancing salsa for ages because I'd been spending more time writing and I suddenly realised how much I'd missed it.

We had a dance in the middle of the shop while Mum finished off rewiring a light fitting.

She also had some rum, although she made a face and asked for more lemonade.

Once we got home I changed into a black top and swishy gold sequined skirt.

My date arrived and Mum asked him three million questions over a cup of tea, mostly about what he did as a sound engineer.

'Leave him alone,' I told her, but he said he didn't mind.

We left for my Auntie's party soon after.

The people celebrating their important birthdays ending in 0, had all met through a Flamenco class lead by a Paraguayan lady, who was loud and sexy and kept hijacking the microphone.

Cheesy music, a buffet with lots of quiche and older people I didn't know; it wasn't the 25th birthday party I'd expected but it felt good to spend the evening with my family.

I see Rosie all the time but rarely see her brothers or my Uncle and Auntie.

'Ooh Colombian,' my uncle said, shaking my date warmly by the hand.

He'd been learning Spanish and couldn't miss this opportunity.

He marched him off to meet people while I blew bubbles from the mini champagne bottles decorating the table.

'Oh you'll like Maria,' I heard him say. 'She's from Paraguay.

I grinned at Rosie who rolled her eyes.

Later, the DJ put on Ricky Martin.

My Auntie leaned over.

'You probably know this one. I think he's from South America.'

It turned into a joke.

Beans? You must like beans, you're South American.

You must like Victor, he's from Chile.

Oh you know this tune; they play it in Bar Salsa.

But you must love Bar Salsa, you're Colombian.

He laughed along and didn't try to hide under the table when a voluptuous, red-cheeked woman came over with arms outstretched to pull him onto the dance floor.

He's a good dancer and unlike a lot of blokes, appears to be in control of his arms and legs.

Rosie wasn't shy about dancing on the roomy dance floor either.

'She's brilliant,' my date said, when he saw her grooving to mo-town and I felt happy because he saw what I saw.

They played reggae and it was like the sun had come out.

We danced together and I didn't tread on his feet.

It felt like a miracle that I knew how to follow. Before learning salsa I'd always been so clumsy and afraid of rhythm.

I knew Mum was watching.

'You look lovely together,' she said, later.

When we got home I found he'd put my present under my duvet.

It was a coffee machine and he'd wrapped it up in a blue, shiny paper.

I love unwrapping presents almost as much as I like getting them.

'That's big,' Mum said, and I knew she was thinking of her kitchen counter.

I slept on the sofa and he slept in my mini bed.

He kissed me goodnight before he went upstairs.

I said something I'd said a while ago in a text message.

This time he replied.

December

❦

Friday 5th December

A CUSTOMER CAME INTO the shop today and asked me if I was the 'blogger'.

I was thrilled!

'When's the novel coming out then?' she asked.

'Well . . . there isn't one yet.'

There are plenty of short stories swimming around my head but no concrete plot for a full length novel. I'm craving one though. Then I can throw everything I've got into it and life will make sense.

Sunday 7th December

I won't be a famous novelist because I'll be delivering a light fitting.

We won't charge for the delivery since we just want the customer to love us and not go to John Lewis. The customer won't offer to pay for the delivery because they assume that's what little shop people do on a Saturday night.

Mum and I will drive around in the dark listening to Magic FM, singing along to the good ones and imitating the husky presenter's voice.

Please call in with your magic moment . . .

But we're not having a magic moment so we won't call in.

My idea of a magic moment is sitting in the sun with a cold beer and a bag of crisps.

When that happens, I'll call in.

Meanwhile I'll grieve for the night in that never happened.

Because I look forward to nights in like kids look forward to Christmas.

Staying at home is my only hope to write a novel. Staying at home and chaining myself to the computer. When the chance passes me by I'm overwhelmed with frustration.

I want to throw pens around and spill ink.

On Saturday night, I spilt a cup of tea over a Christmas card I'd spent ages making for the Date.

It was a collage. I'd cut out all little things that reminded me of him. Like orange juice, chocolate, the Body Works advert, The Simpsons (in Christmas clothes), a cut out from the *quiniela* (Spanish football pools) which said, *Con el fútbol muchos ganan sin tocar el balón* (*In football, lots of people win without touching the ball*) . . . because we'd met through football and we'd not touched the ball . . .

And I'd cut out different letters to spell out his name and Merry Christmas, a bit like a serial killer. I wanted him to open it up at Christmas and remember he had someone special and worth coming back for.

I went to bed after that, comforted by the thought that tomorrow was Sunday and I'd have the whole day to work on a new short story, which I'm calling 'Harry'.

It's a new year's story about realising you don't really like the person you become when you're with certain friends.

This time it's pure fiction.

Well, I suppose one character is based on someone very real. Someone well meaning, I think, but who always drank too much and once peed on my ex's sofa.

Anyway, on Sunday morning, Mum burst into my room and woke me up.

'What have you done with my glove?' she asked.

I didn't know what she was talking about.

'Tea?' she asked.

'No,' I said, pulling my duvet over my nose.

She was leaving for Spain and was full of energy.

'I've got lemon, fennel, normal . . .'

'No, I've got my coffee machine.'

'But don't you want a hot drink first?'

An early start was good. There was so much I wanted to get done.

To begin with, I was going to clean out my underwear drawer and reclaim the five minutes a-day wasted releasing my knickers from knotted tights.

Mum wheeled her suitcase to the door and kissed me goodbye.

After the door slammed I waited for a knock.

She never left without coming back at least once to get something she'd forgotten.

When I thought she wasn't going to come back, I ran upstairs to the loo.

Then came the knock.

I groaned and hurried back downstairs.

Mum was on the door step.

'I don't know where my passport is,' she said.

And that's why I won't be a famous novelist.

Because I'll be too busy looking for a passport.

Monday 8th December

I FOUND THE PASSPORT in a plastic bag stuffed in the corner in the kitchen with all the other plastic bags.

I found it ten hours too late.

Mum left for Spain this morning.

Wednesday 10th December

I WENT TO THE Date's house and watched him pack for Colombia.

I don't know why I watched him pack.

I didn't enjoy it very much.

I should've just said goodbye and left.

Because I started worrying he was going to remember me as being grumpy.

He asked me if I could fit in his suitcase. I tried it and he took a photo. He'll probably show everyone at home and they'll think I'm really needy.

We went for dinner and I cheered up.

Food usually has that effect on me.

Because I wasn't grumpy that he was going.

I'm fine with that. I'm going to write as much as I can while he's away.

Thursday 11th December

MUM IS ALREADY BACK from Spain.

Papa has returned with her.

A lot of people don't understand how they can live like they do, flying back and forwards, seeing each other every two or three weeks.

But their relationship is proof that it works.

It definitely works for me and my brother; it means we each get weeks alone, me in London and him in Barcelona. I suppose that's why we haven't felt under pressure to fly the nest.

I did fly once but I came back.

Sunday 14h December

MY PARENTS ARE DOING the Christmas decorations.

I'm not talking about hanging baubles on the tree or stringing fairy lights across the curtains.

This isn't about tinsel and little angels.

This is serious stuff.

Papa has been painting the living room all day.

Mum is about to drill holes in the wall to put up our new wall lights.

We're finally putting a crystal chandelier in our house.

Bling Bling — go those sleigh bells.

'I bet you've got lovely lights in your house,' customers say.

When you're in the business, the lights in your own home are the last thing you worry about.

In the past we've taken lights off our walls to satisfy customers searching for a perfect match.

This is a new experience.

I'm feeling excited about getting our own bit of razzle-dazzle.

I'd be even more excited if Mum turned off the electrics before she started drilling. But she won't because then Papa won't be able to see where he's painting.

She knocks on the wall.

'Is it wood? Does that sound like wood?'

'Cardboard,' Papa says.

I look up from my notebook.

'I love you mum,' I say.

She starts drilling and my legs go funny.

I'm going to make tea for everyone.

I don't need to ask if they want tea or coffee because I've already made coffee twice today.

Since my date gave me my coffee machine I've never been so enthusiastic about making anyone a drink in my life.

Neither have I bought so much milk in my life or made so much mess.

This morning I used three glasses, two mugs and a pile of spoons.

'Delicious,' Mum said.

'The bubbles are cold,' Papa said.

I whisked his cup away and made another one, using up a few more glasses, mugs and spoons.

'Interesting,' he said. 'It's cold on top and hot below.'

'That's what lattes are like,' Mum said, draining her mug.

After that Mum and I nipped to the shop to get the crystals for our new light.

It felt strange to be in there on a Sunday doing something for ourselves.

We took a long route home scouting for Christmas trees but we didn't see any.

I used to feel like I was the only one in my family who cared about putting up the Christmas trimmings. It always felt a bit touch and go and each year I worried it would never happen.

'When I was little we didn't put the decorations up until Christmas Eve,' Mum insists every year.

Rainbows are spreading across the wall as Mum hooks on the crystals.

Papa keeps on painting, occasionally checking the football scores.

I know we'll get a tree and baubles and some little angels sooner or later.

Tomorrow we'll put a crib in the shop window, complete with mini fire, chickens and a squirrel.

I don't know why I always get so anxious; it always comes together in the end.

That's the magic of Christmas.

Tuesday 16th December

I BOUGHT A MINI camera for my laptop so the Date and I can see each other when we talk on Skype.

It looks like the little helmet of a deep sea diver. I planted it on the top of my screen and couldn't get it to work.

When I finally did, the Date said he could see me fine.

I could hear his mum saying, *'Holaaa!'* in the background.

She came into the picture and I waved like a three year old.

'Hola!' I said back.

Then I went bright red.

Saturday 20th December

I'M NOT GOING OUT tonight because I'm conserving energy.

I haven't had a chance to do my 'Harry' story yet and since we're open up and including Christmas Eve I can't see when I'm going to do it either. I haven't even got a date to meet, for god's sake!

But that's Christmas, you never know what's going to happen.

This morning I walked into the shop and it was littered with reindeers.

They were all over the place, collapsed, decapitated and with their cables trailing between their legs.

They'd been delivered the night before.

It was a massacre. Gold and silver glitter everywhere.

We managed to force their heads in place and plug them in.

They were lovely lit up.

Mum sorted out their mechanisms so their heads moved up and down or side to side.

One of them fell over every time it looked left.

Another one seemed a bit arthritic and creaked every time it looked up from its grazing position.

They attracted a lot of love.

'This is what we need,' one woman said, after telling us her bearded dragon had laid twenty three eggs, 'pets that plug in.'

By lunch time we'd sold them all.

I should've felt tired because I'd planned an evening of salsa at the Peruvian bar the night before.

But I hadn't gone out, even though Rosie and I had just got new dance shoes. Our grandparents had given us extra money for Christmas on the understanding we bought proper shoes.

They go dancing three or four times a week. Gramma has all the catalogues. She sent me some down and I poured over the pictures of gold and silver t-bars and the different inched heels.

We'd gone to that specialist dance shop on the corner of St Martin's Lane.

'Go in with attitude,' the local salsa addict had warned us.

But the shop assistant wasn't a snob and didn't test us on our dancing abilities.

Neither did she mind us trying out all the shoes in the shop, although she might've stopped us if we'd asked for the ballet tutus.

We told each other we'd buy understated pair, perhaps some discreet black ones.

We walked out with sparkly, gold sandals; mine with a diamante buckle on the front.

Our intention to go dancing was pretty strong.

But Christmas is unpredictable.

At 10pm we found ourselves in my local church helping Mum with the Art work.

'You don't have to,' she said, 'but it'd be very nice.'

I couldn't really say no, I hadn't been to church for ages but I couldn't ignore the little voice in my head: *Come on! This is what Christmas is about!*

My brother and his girlfriend were over from Spain so they came to help too.

Soon my fingers were covered in gold paint as I rubbed stars onto a deep, blue sky that my brother helped put up with drawing pins.

The walls were damp and they'd used pins because all the faith in the world wouldn't have kept the heavens up with double-sided tape.

The nativity had moved from Bethlehem to London.

We cut out huge silhouettes from white card of famous London Monuments.

My brother's girlfriend cut out Tower Bridge and Alfie did Big Ben.

It isn't what the parishioners are expecting. Some won't know what to think when they see baby Jesus so near Canary Wharf. But that's a good thing.

Maybe they'll realise something new.

Expectations are not supposed to be fulfilled so easily.

And Christmas wouldn't be Christmas if there were no surprises.

Thursday 25th December.

CHRISTMAS AT MY AUNTIE'S:

I Love it.

Enough said.

I don't like writing about Christmas because it reminds me of having to write about school trips. I could never fully enjoy school trips because in the back of my mind I always knew that when I got home I'd have to write about it and it went a bit like this:

We got the bus to the farm. Then we went for a walk and found some crab apples. Velvet threw a crab apple at me but missed me. I threw a crab apple at

Velvet but hit Nina. Petra ate a crab apple and said it was tasty. Velvet said they were disgusting. Then we had our packed lunch. After lunch we listened to the farmer talk about worms. Then we went back to school.

I never managed to get across how fun the day had been.

Saturday 27th December

I JUST WANT ONE day to myself.

One day to write 'Harry'.

I want to finish it and send it off to Foyles. It's a new year's story so they're more likely to accept it in January than any other month.

I wish I could buy time like you can on a parking meter.

20p for another 10 minutes . . .

Wait, we're in London.

£1 for another 10 minutes . . .

Sunday 28th December

SO MUCH FOR THE credit crunch.

It's official. This has been our busiest Christmas ever.

So it doesn't look like we'll be closing just yet.

Am I surprised? Nope.

'The only the way you'll close the shop is if you leave,' my friends say.

But I want the shop to leave first.

Last time I left, the grass wasn't any greener.

Monday 29th December

'PUTTING YOUR BLOG ON Facebook isn't good enough,' my brother told me.

We were having a drink together, a rare treat, since we hardly ever saw each other.

'Oh,' I said, 'what should I do?'

'You need to be putting your link everywhere,' he said, 'and I mean everywhere.'

Whatever my brother puts his mind to, he seems to achieve. He's a professional aggressive roller blader, clothes designer and business man.

Most recently he's become a Drum 'n' Bass DJ playing in clubs all over Europe.

He says he's rubbish but he's modest like that.

'But how?' I asked.

He rolled up his sleeves and looked at me.

'How much do you want this?'

'More than anything.'

And he launched into an inspirational speech on what I should be doing to promote my blog.

Tuesday 30th December

ONE OF MY NEW Year's resolutions is to be less messy and more organised.

I bought myself a half price calendar and a diary from The National Gallery.

The shop also needs a New Year's face lift.

Today I set to work changing the ceiling display. It involved a lot of stretching, weight-lifting and going up and down the ladder.

I like being up the ladder. It gives me a feeling of being above it all.

That said, on the top rung, when you're holding a heavy light in each hand, your hair caught on a string of crystal and you realise you're about to sneeze, that perspective goes out the window.

'Do you need a hand?' George called up to me.

He'd stopped by with some iced doughnuts.

'No I'm fine!' I said

I sneezed and nearly toppled off the ladder.

'She's an independent woman,' he said, to no one in particular.

I think he meant stubborn.

George has taken to stopping by longer recently. Today Mum was helping him out with some bank forms he had to send off. He never wants tea, just a cup of water, the 'good stuff', he calls it.

He sat by the counter and commented on the world while I continued shifting light fittings around. It was quite a work-out, which is why I'm not too bothered about adding 'get fit' to my list of resolutions.

To be honest, I haven't really got a list of resolutions yet.

I'm an all or nothing sort of person and if I put pen to paper I'll get depressed by the insurmountable challenges I'll set myself.

I'd thought about New Year changes this morning as I'd grieved for the items I'd carelessly lost in a club on Saturday.

Me and my brother had meant to go for one drink but had ended up going out until the early hours. I suppose we'd got overexcited.

'I look like I should be in a library!' I cried over the music.

And I'd pushed my glasses onto my head and lost them.

I didn't even realise I'd lost them until I'd walked outside and realised I couldn't see anything.

I'd lost a favourite jumper too.

This morning I'd sobbed into my coffee and thought:

'Idiot.'

And I'd decided to give up drinking forever.

Then I'd thought six months was a more achievable target.

But then I'd thought it might get a bit dull for my friends and my date, so maybe I would give it up for just three months.

Or perhaps I would only drink on weekends.

But of course that would contradict the point of not drinking, which was to have a clear mind so I could write more on weekends.

Anyway, I balanced on one foot and did the 'lunging tortoise' yoga move, or whatever it was, to hang the lights onto the ceiling hook. I pulled my hair free and got down from the ladder.

Anthony, the local evangelical healer man was at the door and I let him in.

'Merry Christmas Princess Emma,' he said, beaming. 'The Holy Spirit told me to come here and get white vinyl paint.'

I used to find Anthony a bit strange but you get used to anything in this shop.

'Vinyl paint? He should've sent you to the Builder's Merchant,' I told him.

He walked up to the counter to where Mum was tidying up.

'Yes, but they are closed,' he said.

'I think the Holy Spirit should've got you up and out a bit earlier,' Mum said, looking at her watch.

But Mum being Mum, she went upstairs and had a look anyway. And lo and behold, she found a full pot of white vinyl paint, although she thought it might've gone off and said it smelled funny.

Anthony was delighted.

'Have a blessed and happy New Year!' he cried, as he left.

'You too,' I say, meaning it.

I went back up my ladder and my perspective changed once more. I gave up all thoughts of punishing resolutions and carried on sorting out the ceiling.

Wednesday 31stth December

VELVET IS HAVING A New Year's party at her house.

Theme: Cowboys and Indians.

Advantages:
House party is cheap
No queues
Nice people

Disadvantages:
North London = mission
I'll have to go on the tube dressed as a cowboy/Indian
I won't wake up feeling like a new woman
I won't write 'Harry'

January

❧

Thursday 1st January

'YOU'RE A WRITER ALREADY,' people say. 'You don't have to be published.'

There's a two page spread about writing to not get published in the magazine in the loo. I keep meaning to write to the magazine pointing out the contradiction but by the time I've washed my hands I've lost the motivation.

I almost went to Velvet's party. I thought about what I could wear as a cowgirl.

And then I thought of 'Harry' and how great it would be to send a short story off on the first day of New Year.

So I stayed at home.

Papa had the Spanish television on for the run up to the bells.

'That looks pre-recorded,' Mum said, about the concert.

The presenters stood on balconies overlooking the Plaza del Sol, the women freezing in their strapless dresses.

We ate a grape for each dong of the bell. I remember it being much harder when I was little. I suppose because I had a smaller mouth and couldn't chew quick enough.

I felt happy. I'd done the right thing staying in.

Tomorrow I would wake up without a hangover and use the whole day to push forward with my writing. I'd finish my short story and I'd send it off to Foyles. After that I'd forget short stories and concentrate on coming up with a plot for a novel.

I could finish a novel in a couple of months if only I had a decent plot. I'd turn into a hermit for a while.

I'd keep my head down, stay in, get up earlier, not drink . . .

As I was thinking about this strategy, my mobile rang.

It was my date, calling from Colombia.

'Happy New Year!' he cried, excitedly. 'Where are you?'

He'd expected music in the background, the sound of a party.

'What you mean you're at home?'

He sounded disappointed.

I suddenly got that horrible feeling in my stomach. I'd done the wrong thing. I was supposed to be at Velvet's party with all the other Cowboys and Indians.

'I wanted to finish a short story,' I said, feeling stupid.

'But it's New Year! You're allowed to go out!'

'I know, but I just wanted to have one good day to write . . .'

He said he was near the beach having dinner.

He said, later he was going to a club with some friends he'd just made.

In the end he said, 'good for you' or something like that. I didn't really hear. It was too late, the damage was done.

He was cool.

And I was a geek.

I lay in bed thinking about him in his hot country, in a club full of half-dressed *mamasitas*.

I thought how easy it would be to forget out there.

Forget everything and everyone for one night.

I didn't get to sleep for ages.

Oh, but that was yesterday.

Today I got up.

And I wrote.

And I wrote some more.

At 9pm I mailed 'Harry' to Tales of the Decongested.

I have a choice to do what I really want to do, as long as I can accept that with a choice comes a sacrifice.

Friday 2nd January

NEW YEAR'S DAY PASSED without a sign of life from my date.

I sent him a text message, hoping he was having a good time, telling him I felt like a geek.

I supposed he was on the beach with his new friends.

I could taste the rum. I could see the girls in bikini at the edge of the sparkling water, their skins golden.

I wondered if he'd been able to resist.

Had he seen them and then thought of me, sitting at my kitchen table in my hoodie and tracksuit bottoms tapping away on my laptop.

Geek or *mamasita*?

And would I forgive him if he hadn't resisted?

Sun, rum, party, another continent . . .

I could understand. Though understanding wouldn't make it hurt any less.

These thoughts washed over me as I sat in front of the TV with Papa.

I tried to push them away, tried not to think about it.

My mobile vibrated and I held my breath as I opened the message.

I expected the disappointment to weigh down on me like an 8-arm brass chandelier, because I expected it to be a message from my phone company wishing me a happy new year and a special offer on ringtones.

'The best thing of 2008 was by far meeting you,' the message said. 'The best thing of 2009 is to be with you. I love you my geek.'

I beamed.

Papa rolled his eyes.

I beamed some more.

Papa changed the channel.

Tuesday 6th January

TODAY WAS *El Día de los Reyes*.

The coming of the three Kings.

Christmas, 'Spanish Style'.

A paella for 40 people at my Spanish Auntie's.

Mmmmmmm . . .

Enough said.

Friday 9th January

IF WE ONLY INVITED current staff to our belated Staff Christmas party, it would just be me and Mum.

Not much of a party.

So we always invite past staff too, which means Petra and Alfie.

Papa comes obviously and Alfie brings his wife.

Petra and I were last to arrive because we'd gone for a drink with Nina. She's my optician now although I can't take her seriously and giggle every time she asks me to read the letters projected on the wall.

The big news is Nina's getting married. Things had been heading that way since her parents approved the match.

You can get a lot of conversation out of getting married. More so when it's a friend you've known since you were eight years old.

I can still see her sitting by me on the school bus in that yellow gym top that was always miles too big for her.

She used to say she wanted to get married at 24. Well, she'll be 26. Not far off.

We talked about rings for ages. It'd taken her hours to choose one, not because they were all so different but rather because they all looked virtually the same.

I said I wanted a gold wedding ring. But I think I just said that to be different.

Between rings, dresses and honeymoons, we ended up having three beers and getting to my house after everybody else.

At home the preparations were in full swing.

Papa had the olives out and the wine open. Funny that he's not a big fan of parties and hardly ever drinks and yet is such a good host.

We were just taking our coats off when he announced the news.

'I met a very nice bloke for you today in the shop.'

'She's already got one!' Mum called from the kitchen.

And I had no intention of replacing him either, especially after such a lovely text message. Petra wasn't looking for a replacement either, even though she'd been with her bloke at least 7 years.

'What about your cousin?'

Rosie's last date, Alejandro, had been deported back to South America so I knew she was free and single.

'What's he like?'

'He's very nice,' Papa said. 'I spoke to him for some time.'

This was breaking news.

My dad isn't a small talk man and has never been one to chat to young men. Perhaps the key was this young man was Spanish.

Either way, the idea of setting Rosie up was rather exciting.

'He's coming tomorrow morning to collect a table lamp,' Mum said.

I rang Rosie straight away and told her to come to the shop after yoga.

'I can't,' she said, 'I'm going to my Mums'.'

Disaster.

'But send him my love,' she giggled, 'and get his number!'

So I have to lure him into conversation and get his number . . . for my cousin.

Possible?

We will see.

Saturday 10th January

I GOT TO THE shop today and felt like everything was thick with dust. So I grabbed the Clean 'n' Fresh window cleaner and started having a go at everything.

I use window cleaner because the nozzle on the polish has fallen off.

In fact the nozzle on the polish always falls off. I'm like the dad in My Big Fat Greek Wedding. I'll use window cleaner on my hands if I'm desperate.

Anyway, so I had all the picture frames in the middle of the floor when this young man came in and told me, in a Spanish accent, that he'd come to collect a table lamp.

He was blue-eyed, fair-skinned and if he hadn't spoken I wouldn't have guessed he was the one. I might've thought he was French actually because there seem to be a lot of French moving into the area.

'Yes, I was warned,' I said.

I don't think he understood.

His collection was clearly marked which made the operation all a bit smooth, leaving little opportunity for conversation. I was suddenly worried he was going to leave without me extracting any information.

'Oh you met my Dad, didn't you?' I said, scrabbling for something to say.

Not the most seductive line.

'Yes, you are the traveller, no?'

'Uh . . . yes.'

I didn't know what Papa had been saying but he's inclined to exaggerate.

According to his work colleagues I've already published many books and am on track to receive a Nobel Prize.

At least it gave an opening to talk.

So I really went for it.

Luckily he was friendly and clearly not in a hurry to get away.

I had no idea how I was supposed to get his number though. To make it worse, the shop phone didn't stop ringing.

Gramma rang and I told her I was busy.

My Auntie rang and I told her I was busy.

A customer rang and I told him I was busy.

It made me look like I was really desperate to talk to him. The transaction was done and anyone else would've said a final thank you and walked out of the shop by now.

I heard myself say, 'Oh you live around here? Wow, we could meet up.'

And I could imagine my date despairing at the conversation because it sounded like I was flirting.

But I really was on a mission to get his number for Rosie. It was something I'd never attempted to do before and it felt quite gutsy.

Mum walked in while we were chatting about his hometown and offered him a cup of tea.

Good move, I thought.

He told us he lived near Valencia.

Rosie and I had been talking about going to Valencia for the festivals in March.

Funny that.

Funnier still that after a cup of tea he was inviting us to stay at his house.

Not just a blind date, I was setting up a blind holiday.

I wasn't even sure of his name until he gave me his email.

Sergio Solozano Sosa.

Not the easiest name for someone like me, someone with a lisp.

Rosie Solozano Sosa,

Gramma might find it hard to say too.

Monday 12th January

I went on Facebook at the shop.

The Date had sent me a message saying he was in Miami.

'What do you think of when I say Miami', I asked Mum.

'Crocodiles.'

'Oh.'
I'd thought of convertibles and half-dressed woman.
I rang Rosie in the afternoon.
'What do you think of when I say Miami?'
'Bad clubs and white suits.'
Still, I wish I was there.

Tuesday 13th January

IT WAS QUIET IN the shop today so I spent half an hour sending my blog link to people on Facebook. I stopped when a pop up box told me that my activity was annoying.

I can't remember the exact words but Facebook was definitely telling me off.

So I joined writers' groups instead and left my link on their wall.

I became a fan of Salt Publishing even though I'd no idea who they were.

I don't know if anyone bothers to follows links, I know I don't, but I keep thinking of what my brother said. I have to do much, much more to get my work out there.

Wednesday 14st January

I HOPE SERGIO ISN'T regretting inviting us to his house because we've just booked our flights to Valencia. It was raining all day and I was fed up so I bombarded Rosie until she agreed.

Friday 16th January

TODAY I FILLED THE window with ex-display picture frames.

I wanted to get things moving so I was clearing them for peanuts.

'I thought you were closing at Christmas,' more than one customer has said.

We added 'Huge Reductions' under the Closing sign but the end is hardly in sight.

We've been busier than ever and have no intention of going while we're still selling stock.

A woman came in and pointed vaguely at one of the frames.

'I want the one for a pound,' she said.

'It's scratched,' I warned her.

'What size is it?'

'Five by seven.'

I handed her the frame.

'Now I measured the photo,' she said, running her finger along the glass. 'It's six this way and eight across.'

'Then you want a six by eight.'

'No, that's too big.'

'But . . .' I frowned. 'You said you measured it as a six by eight.'

'I'll take a risk,' she said, pushing the coin into my hand.

I wanted to call after her, tell her she was making a big mistake.

But they say the customer is always right.

A smart young man in a cashmere coat and pale blue shirt came up to the counter.

'I want a screw-in push-in bulb please,' he said, confidently.

'Sorry?'

'A screw-in push-in bulb. 60 watts.'

'It either screws in or pushes in. It can't be both'

'Oh. I'll just have a 60 watt one then.'

'O–kay,' I said, smiling slightly. 'A 60 watt screw or bayonet?'

He shrugged.

'There isn't a big difference is there?'

But again, the customer is always right.

Another woman was after a specific light shade.

I told her we were unlikely to order from that company anymore.

'We want to clear what we have,' I explained, 'Because we're closing.'

'You've been closing down for a long time,' she said, looking at me over her severe black glasses.

'Uh . . . well . . .' I was aware it'd been dragging on but it wasn't like we could shove all these lights under our bed. 'I suppose it has been a few months.'

'No,' she said. 'You've been closing down for at least five years.'

Five years! And to think I hadn't realised.

Now really, how can all customers be right if half of them think the flowery light above my head is Art Deco?

That's just silly.

Which is not the same as saying *they* are silly.

Most of them are wonderful and fantastically loyal.

Even the occasional good humoured barterers can be fun. Barterers who choose to ignore price labels, even when they are big, red and have 'half price' scrawled across them.

Like the south London plasterer who finally narrowed his choice down to two chandeliers.

'Come on. Two hundred for both,' he pushed. 'I'll give you the cash now.'

'I'll buy them myself for that,' I said, quoting Mum.

'Come on love, two hundred or I'm going.'

'I'm not arguing anymore.'

Mum once told someone to keep his money and buy some crisps.

'Come on love, we're having fun!'

'260. Take it or leave it. '

'You're difficult. Do you have a boyfriend?'

'Yes.'

'I feel sorry for him.'

'He's newish.'

'I don't want to know what happened to the last one!'

'He went to Vietnam.'

That made him laugh and I realised I wasn't helping my cause.

'I bet he did. I'm going to join him in a minute.'

'Don't be so rude,' I said.

Nowadays when customers push me too far I suggest they go to Argos. They really hate that.

'Come on love, let's not muck about,' he insisted. 'I'll give you 210, bulbs included.'

He stuck his hand out. I wasn't going to shake it.

'260,' I said.

'210.'

'250!'

'220.'

We stared each other in the eyes.

Most of the time, it's a pretty level playing field in my shop.

We win some. We lose some.

It just wouldn't work if the customer was always right.

Saturday 17th January

'HARRY' HAS BEEN ACCEPTED! My second story in a row!

I danced around my room grinning for a while then texted everyone who might care.

I decided to tell my date when he arrived at the airport.

But later he sent me a text message: 'Will you still love me if I come back a week later?'

There was a possible job in Miami which would pay for his flight back.

'No,' I replied.

Then thought better of it.

'Of course.'

Anyway, this isn't going to be my last story. I intend to write lots more. I intend to write books and films and plays. I'm so happy it got in! I'm so happy I don't even care that I have to go to Birmingham tomorrow, on a Sunday, my sacred day off.

Sunday 18th January

EVERY YEAR WE GO to Birmingham for the Light Show.

Every year we say we'll go early.

'Leave at nine?' Mum suggested the night before.

'Yeah, at the latest,' I agreed.

I woke up at 8.51. Plenty of time.

We were still in our pyjamas at ten, eating toast and registering our tickets for the show.

'Oops, I've put you were born in 1951,' Mum said.

My name badge said I was the Manager.

It also said I was the Designer/Specifier.

'What does that even mean?'

'It means you specify what you want,' Mum said.

'Mmm . . .'

So could I ask for a tortoise lamp shade with my name on it?

No, I didn't think so.

Could I ask for a chandelier covered in purple sequins?

Unlikely.

I couldn't specify anything really.

We arrived at lunchtime and met up with some fellow shopkeepers.

They were a team of mother and son who were clearly keener retailers than us having arrived at the same time as I got up. The son had contacted me after reading my blog. He'd found it by googling Closing Down Shops, which was a bit morbid.

'So what sells best then?' I asked him, later in the day.

He hesitated, smiling a little nervously.

'Come on, our shops are on different sides of the country!' I said.

He mumbled something about 'trade secrets'.

I was baffled. We were about as threatening as Woolworths.

Remember Woolworths?

He offered some information a little reluctantly and Mum and I trundled off to the suggested wholesalers where we succumbed to a free glass of wine.

At one point the rep tried to top up our glass.

'No,' I said, 'Or we might buy the whole lot.'

He looked hopeful and hovered nearby with the rest of the bottle.

I suppose I understand why the son might've felt a need to be secretive.

To the naked eye, we appear to be just small time shopkeepers.

Ah, but we are so much more.

The trouble is I never know who should know what.

So when we were called over by the friendly son and mother to the stand of a major distributer, that *we* were probably the only people who didn't buy from, I felt a little apprehensive.

Were we their competition? Did they know my dad? Had my dad copied their lights or had they copied us?

'This girl is very clever!' the mother gushed to one of the company own-
ers. 'You should read what she writes.'

'It's a blog,' I said, 'about our lighting shop.'

At which point Mum developed a twitch.

Had I said too much?

A rep from the same company sat down beside me.

'Oh yes? So who are you then?' he asked, cheerfully.

'In what sense?' I said. 'I am many things.'

He looked at me like I was an idiot.

'Your name,' he said.

'Ah.'

It was hardly a secret; it was hanging around my neck.

I was Miss Emily Benet, Manager, Designer and Specifier.

If he was impressed, he didn't show it.

A few moments later he got up and wandered off.

I threw caution to the wind and took one of their free sweets.

While I was sucking my sweet the Date called me. The line was crackly
but I just about made out that the job had been cancelled and he was coming back as planned, in two days.

Monday 19th January

I'VE INVITED SO MANY people to Foyles, including Sergio.

I thought it would be the perfect opportunity for Rosie and him to finally meet, fall in love and get married etc. I've also invited Pedro, a friend of the Date. He's a camera man. If Sergio isn't the one, then maybe Pedro is.

Wednesday 21th January

My date came back from his travels with a bear hug and coffee beans covered in chocolate.

It was our first date in six weeks and I wanted to watch something heart-warming, something that echoed the happy feeling I had inside.

The Indian millionaire film was supposed to be the feel-good movie of the year.

'I cried all the way through,' Rosie said.

I assumed she meant cried with happiness.

But whoever wrote the poster for it needs to watch the film first.

Feel-good factor?

I would have felt better if I'd stuck my finger in the mains tester.

In no time, I was blubbing like a toddler who'd got lost in a room full of clowns.

And I really don't like clowns.

In fact the only thing that could've made this film more depressing was if they'd added a few clowns dancing to bhangra in the background.

Kids sleeping in rubbish, diving through poo, fighting for survival . . . It wasn't exactly sunny material, was it?

My maternal instincts were on over-drive.

How was I possibly going to save all these little children?

My date glanced at me sideways and noticed the gleam of snot and tears.

He rubbed my knee. But it wasn't enough.

I was still snivelling when I got home.

The thing is, I'm an impulsive sort of person and being impulsive when you've got access to internet has its consequences.

A few clicks later and I found myself agreeing to sponsor a child.

I didn't know who the child was or where they came from. All I knew was that I was going to have to cancel my *Time Out* subscription a bit sharpish.

Sunday 25th January

PEDRO AND SERGIO CAN both come to the reading.

Rosie, however, is in Ireland that weekend. So close yet so far.

Monday 26th January

I WAS PROCRASTINATING BECAUSE I was fed up of dressing the same model over and over again. It's our waterfall chandelier and it's our best seller, which is why I'm always dressing it over and over again.

So I logged in on Facebook and opened my inbox to find this:

Hi Emily,

Salt Publishing here . . . . I was very taken with your blog . . . . . .
think there's something we could do . . . .
great idea . . . well executed . . . . might need a little work
. . . . I've spoken to our fiction editor . . . . certainly
interested. Could you drop her a line with an outline proposal . .
. . . ?

My thinking is that this would be highly marketable to shop work-
ers in all major cities . . . Let's talk about it.

Thanks . . . . . I love it.
All best
C . . .

'Oh my God,' I said. 'Mum, read this.'

I needed her to tell me it wasn't a mail out to all their Facebook fan members.

'Oh,' she said.

And we just looked at each other, neither of us quite believing what we'd just read.

Monday 26th January (2 minutes later)

'Should I write excited?' I asked Mum.

'Are you excited?'

'Of course!'

'Then yes.'

So I replied to saying I was excited and very interested and I would send an outline as soon as possible.

Tuesday 27th January

I WROTE *Painting Pears* for three years, but the hardest part was writing the synopsis.

Now I feel a block. I have to write an outline and I can't do it.

This is the best opportunity I've ever been given and the fear of getting it wrong has frozen me.

I'm sitting in front of the screen not moving.

My date rings and tells me not to worry.

But I *am* worried; it's in my stomach, like the knot at the end of a balloon.

Wednesday 28th January

THE DATE SENT ME a message early this morning.

'Check your mail, it might help ☺'

He'd had insomnia and had written an outline for me.

'Now you just have to put it into your own voice,' he said, brightly.

I felt overwhelmed with gratitude.

'Most people just watch telly when they can't sleep!' I gushed to just about anyone who would listen. 'This guy is amazing!'

Later, I edited the outline and sent it to the publishers.

I can't think about anything else.

This is my dream. It's all I've ever wanted to do.

I couldn't stop checking my mail today. I had to discipline myself to checking it only once I'd made a tier of crystal on a chandelier. It ended up more like every quarter of a tier though.

They haven't replied yet but they've both added me as a friend on Facebook, which is partly why I'm keeping to my status: *Reading short story at Foyles on Friday.*

Thursday 29th January

RITA USED TO HAVE the market stall in front of our shop.

She's known me since I was as big as a bedside table lamp.

I watched her looking at the picture frames today and it dawned on me that I'd never given her a hug. I think it might have something to do with that message from the publishers. I'm feeling a lot of love at the moment.

'How are you?' I said, rubbing her arm.

'Alright . . .' She glanced at the door. 'Don't you get afraid when you're in here all by yourself?'

I noticed that I'd left the yellow Stanley knife on the display shelf.

'No, not really,' I said.

I reached over and pocketed the knife.

'Do you remember the man who took the clock?' she said.

'Yes. My brother got it back though.'

He'd gone for the thief like a tiger.

He'd jumped so high he'd got the guy's cap as well as the clock.

'You should keep the door shut,' Rita said.

'But then no one will come in.'

I spotted a screwdriver on the floor and picked it up.

Perhaps I should be more worried. The shop was armed.

'It's not that easy to steal a chandelier,' I said.

Unless it's lying on the floor.

'And you'd probably break it before you got too far.'

'Well . . .' she said.

Frankly, I'm in danger of being knocked out before anyone's even come in.

It's the low hanging lights. We mean to hang them low only down the sides, but they creep nearer the middle, getting lower each time we re-hang the ceiling.

'We need to make them visible,' Papa always says.

'I've seen them hung really, *really* low in a shop in Ireland,' Mum said.

The pain if you stand up underneath one and hit your head can be pretty full on.

Sometimes you see colours and butterflies and fat yellow stars like in a Disney film.

If you don't get concussed by a light then you get caught up in the crystal.

The other day I got hooked up in the shop window.

I was crawling around the picture frames when my hair was pulled back by a gold-plated special offer.

The more I struggled the more tangled I became.

I was stuck.

Passersby looked on and wondered what sort of bulb I took. Maybe they thought my transformer had packed up.

Shoplifters could've cleared the whole shop out in the time it took me to break free.

We call them Dippers.

They work in twos or threes.

One of them fires endless questions at you while the other does the stealing.

'How much is that light?' they'll say, pointing at the ceiling. 'Is that good for a bedroom?

I'll feel something is wrong.

'What about that one?' they keep on, 'is that good for the kitchen?'

They point upwards to keep my eyes away from their friend who is either trying to nick stuff from the front of the shop or slip pass me to get to the till.

I'm less worried about offending now than I used to be.

I don't follow the finger.

'Yes, it's great for the bedroom,' I say flatly. 'It's great for the kitchen. In fact, you can put that light anywhere you want to.'

'What, *that* one?' they insist.

I stare ahead.

'Yep.'

'What about *that* one?'

'Yep. Perfect.'

Someone tried to take a bulb without paying for it once.

I was too annoyed to be afraid and pulled it out of his hand.

He told me to stick it up my *derriere*.

Charming, I thought, but I was smug I'd got it back, even if I was more snatching monkey than leaping tiger.

Thursday p.m.

READING CANCELLED.

Room at Foyles double-booked.

New reading scheduled for next week.

Facebook status: *Reading at Foyles NEXT FRIDAY*.

It's very annoying because so many people were going to come.

The Date won't be able to make it next week.

At least Rosie will.

But what about Sergio and Pedro?

Friday 30th January

TODAY IT CAME. THE mail I've been dreaming about all my life. I've underlined the part that i particularly enjoyed, (understatement of the year).

Hi Emily,

Thanks for getting in touch . . . . I too was thinking that . .
. . . . . . would work brilliantly. The positive of this would be that . . .
. . . .

I have attached a contract . . . . the sooner we start promoting,
the better! . . . . I would love to meet up . . . . . .

. . . . . . best wishes from us both and I'm so looking forward to work-
ing with you.
J . . .

I was so excited.

I told my date and my brother.

I told Seb because I wanted to tell a fellow writer.

'Enjoy the champagne!' Seb texted.

But I was the kind of child who had to finish their homework before she could enjoy playing.

I didn't want to celebrate. I just wanted to get started on the book.

'Can I have some days off?' I asked Mum.

'No.'

'Really?'

'Well, you'll need to be at the shop to get more material for your book.'

Funny how this life changing moment is not going to change my immediate life at all; tomorrow I'll be making crystal strings as if nothing unusual had happened.

Saturday 31st January

WE ALL MET UP yesterday even though Foyles was cancelled.

Petra came and so did Nina. My date came with a flower hair clip.

'Congratulations my little author,' he said, giving me a kiss. 'I didn't bring you real flowers because you'd have to carry them.'

I thought that was really sweet.

When he left to get us drinks Nina leaned towards me.

'Em, you're really good,' she said.

'Why?'

'Because you look happy even though he didn't bring you real flowers.'

'But I like the hair clip.'

'Oh,' she said. 'I see.'

I sent Sergio a text message telling him to come straight to the bar.

He didn't appear.

I rang him but he didn't answer.

Oh well, I thought, no harm done since Rosie wasn't coming either.

An hour later he rang from his home.

'I was waiting at the station,' he said. 'I left my phone at my house.'

I felt bad. I should've known.

He came back out anyway.

'What do you want to drink?' I asked.
'Just a coke,' he said.
And that's when I knew he wasn't the one for Rosie.

February

❦

Monday 2nd February

MY GUMS ARE STILL bleeding and Blanche, sloshed as usual, told me to buy special mouthwash from the dentist.

'I know you won't do it,' she said.

So I did.

I walked up to the dentist and handed over my fiver.

But the receptionist had other ideas.

'Do you think *you* are a dentist? How do you know what you need?' she said. 'I'll book you an appointment now.'

To be fair the dentist who saw me was miles better than the last one who saw me.

This one showed me a diagram.

After that she gave me four injections in one side of my mouth.

I tried to think happy thoughts as she dug the oral claw hammer between my teeth.

I tried to sing a soothing song in my head.

I wanted to ask her if she'd wanted to be a dentist when she was little.

Maybe this child I was sponsoring would want to be a dentist.

Fifteen minutes later I was back in front of the sullen receptionist, my face half paralysed.

'You're bleeding,' she said.

I was also dribbling all over myself but she didn't mention that.

She pointed to the special offer electric toothbrushes.

'How much?'

'Eighty pounds'

I winced.

'Your teeth are going to fall out,' she said, looking bored.

So I bought the toothbrush.

And floss. And mouthwash. And special toothpaste for sensitive teeth.

When I got home I found I'd received news from the sponsorship programme.

The child is a little boy from Guatemala.

He looks out grumpily from the photo as if someone's interrupted his playtime.

I tried but I couldn't see his teeth.

They can't be that bad though; he's only three and hasn't had them very long.

Tuesday 3rd February

GEORGE CAME IN WHILE I was practising reading 'Harry' out loud.

He sat down at the counter and asked for the 'good stuff'.

'So,' he said, when I'd given him his water, 'I won't be needing to get you one of those this year.'

He was looking at the dusty Valentines' card still stuck on the wall.

He'd sent it to me last year and signed it, 'an old flame.'

'You're courting now so he can get you one.'

I grinned.

'I don't know if he'll do anything,' I said.

'He must get you a card!' he cried. 'What sort of man doesn't get his valentine a card?'

But you can never be sure.

I haven't mentioned Valentine's Day and nor has he.

Wednesday 4th February

I HAD A CHAT with Mum's lawyer friend who's been looking through my publishing contract.

'Well,' she said. 'It looks like you won't be able to give up the day job just yet then.'

'No, I know.'

If it'd been about money I would've given up writing ages ago.

Perhaps I'd have persevered at the estate agents instead.

Although in these uncertain times I'd have been the first to be fired.

'I didn't realise you didn't have a degree,' one of the bosses had said on my last day, as if he wouldn't have dreamed of employing me if he'd known. 'Perhaps you should go to secretary school.'

When I got home I thought of all these things I wish I'd said.

And I thought, when I finally publish a book I'll send it to you, to show I'm not just someone rubbish at taking phone calls and passing on messages.

Thursday 5th February

I WAS ON THE phone to Mum when a man came into the shop with a pile of *Guardian* newspapers.

Late 40s, cross-eyed and grey-haired, he was wearing a blue anorak with a name badge around his neck. Except it wasn't a name badge because it didn't have his name on it.

In fact it looked like he'd cut out a piece of cereal box and laminated it himself with sellotape.

'Mum, I'll call you back.'

'I'm selling for the children,' he said in broken English, putting a newspaper down on the counter in front of me.

He ran his finger under the typed price.

'90p. Very cheap.'

I looked at the paper for a clue but I didn't get it.

'What are you doing?'

'I'm doing for the church.'

'What are you doing for the church?'

'I get money for children. I am charity.'

'What charity?'

'For the church.'

'I don't understand. Who are you?'

He touched his chest, 'I am . . .' he paused, struggling with the word that came out sounding very French, '*Volontaaaire.*'

'But why are you selling the *Guardian* for charity?'

Usually people come in with a badge and a money collection tin and we give them something because it's quicker than not giving them something.

'It's good,' he said, 'got sport section . . .'

'I know what the *Guardian* is,' I said, frowning, 'but why are you selling it to me for charity for the same price as Costcutter?'

'For the children. I am charity.'

'Yes but . . .'

'For church . . .'

I could see I wasn't making much headway in my investigation so I ended up buying a newspaper and giving him 10p over the odds.

I checked that it was today's date, which it was, and called Mum back.

'I think I've just bought a stolen *Guardian*.'

'Ah,' she said.

'I don't really know how it happened.'

I never knowingly buy things that have fallen off the back of the lorry because it would be like encouraging someone to steal from my shop. This is South East London and goods are forever falling off the back of vehicles. Presumably that's why there are so many traffic jams.

Watches, fake Louis Vuitton bags, cameras, bubble bath, mobiles, iPods and now, the *Guardian*.

Only last week someone tried to sell me a king-size bed.

'I over-ordered,' the lad said.

Apart from the fact I can only just fit a single bed in my room, I couldn't help thinking how implausible it sounded.

You'd think you'd take the bed back to the shop, wouldn't you?

It's not like an extra pair of tights that you end up keeping because you know they'll come in handy sooner or later.

'I don't need one, thank you,' I said, 'But good luck.'

Good luck? I thought to myself after. Why on earth would I wish him good luck?

But I worry if I'm not super polite the next thing they'll be trying to flog will be my chandeliers, and I'm quite happy to do that by myself, thank you very much.

Friday 6th February

ROSIE AND HER PARENTS were in the cafe when I arrived at Foyles.

Sergio came in a moment later.

'*Hola,*' Rosie said, in her best accent.

There wasn't a spark when their eyes met.

No thunder, just the clatter of cutlery.

'Wow,' he said, 'the whole family.'

'Yes,' I said, and didn't know if I was supposed to apologise.

We went upstairs to the 'the gallery' room.

I saved seats at the front row for my parents.

Sergio embarked on a complicated conversation about his job situation. He'd already told me about it in English and Spanish but I still didn't understand.

My uncle got involved but I could tell Rosie was drifting.

I just wanted to be quiet and sip my wine. I wasn't on until the second half which I was glad about because both Petra and Nina were running late.

Pedro and my parents came as it was about to start.

Pedro slipped into the seat by Sergio. He looked good in a pale blue T-shirt. I wondered if Rosie had seen him and what she thought.

The stories began and they were pretty intense.

A lot of vaginas and masturbation, which made me shift uncomfortably in my seat.

I'm not sure if I felt uncomfortable because I'm a prude or because my parents were listening two seats away. My guess is I'm a prude. I'm not sure I'll ever be able to write about sex; I think I'll always resort to fluttering curtains.

When it came to my go I had the usual shaky leg.

I stood up and saw that Petra and Nina had slipped in at the back. A young man was standing beside Nina, the fiancé I'd not yet met. I wondered what they'd thought of the masturbation so far.

Pedro left his seat and stood at the back taking photos. It surprised me but then he *is* a camera man so it shouldn't have. And anyway, he hadn't come to hear the story, he'd come to meet my cousin, we both knew that.

The story went down well. It's amazing catching a listener's eye and seeing they're really engaging with what you're reading.

The best thing is when they laugh. I love it when people laugh.

After the reading everyone had to rush off. Everyone, that is, except me, Rosie and Pedro.

Perfect.

We went for a drink nearby and Pedro suggested we went to his friend's party.

Rosie didn't think it twice. She didn't even ask where the party was.

'Why not?' she said.

Chemistry at last.

Thursday 12th February

I MADE THE MISTAKE of telling the Date I thought Valentine's Day was stupid.

'You didn't!' Nina cried, when I told her. 'What were you thinking?'

'I don't know! I got nervous!'

'Now he's not going to do anything!'

She's expecting her fiancé to propose to her on Valentine's.

They've already organised their wedding and honeymoon, now he just needs to get down on one knee.

It's all backwards in their tradition, her words not mine.

'But it's so commercial, isn't it?' I sighed. 'It is though, isn't it?'

Apart from a plasma lamp and a picture frame with hearts on it, we haven't really profited from the event.

Nina thought I'd blown it.

'I don't know how you're going to backtrack now.'

I had to hang up because I had customers. They were two huge Nigerian blokes, so tall they were in danger of being knocked out by the chandeliers.

One of them was holding an electric hair clippers with mismatched cable perilously taped together.

It looked about as safe as rain in a light shop.

They wanted an adaptor for its two-pin plug. I suggested changing the plug altogether and asked if I should do it for them.

I got my wire strippers and screwdriver.

They watched me closely. They weren't expecting I could use a tool because I was wearing lipstick.

One of them sat on the stool opposite me and leant over the counter. He had watery eyes and badly pockmarked skin.

'You are not British. Where are you from?'

'I am, sort of. Spanish-English.'

'Spanish . . .' he paused. *'Hola.'*

'Hola.'

'Como está?'

'Bien . . .'

'Would you marry a black man?'

The question just popped out of nowhere and I was so surprised I couldn't answer.

What black man was he talking about?

Where from?

Couldn't he be more specific?

Was he talking about himself?

I thought of my date. Why would I marry a random black man when I already had a date?

The tension was palpable and it grew with every second I delayed in answering.

'Well I have a boyfriend so . . .'

'I'm not asking you if you have a boyfriend,' he interrupted, staring at me. 'I'm asking if you would marry a black man.'

'That's a stupid question.'

His friend, who'd been standing by his side looking uncomfortable, agreed.

'Yeah, it's a stupid question.'

'Look,' I said, 'I would marry someone who has a good heart and is well-suited to me, colour doesn't come into it.'

There was silence.

My interrogator nodded. 'Good answer.'

The atmosphere relaxed. The interrogator's friend tried to engage me in conversation.

'So how many Valentine's days have you celebrated with your boyfriend?'

'None . . . it's the first one.'

He laughed, as if to say that it doesn't really count then.

But I learned a while ago that the customer isn't always right.

Saturday 14th February

MY DATE OPENED THE door and grinned.

Something was different.

I stepped into the corridor and he wouldn't let me go on further.

My heart soared.

I smelt a surprise and it smelt delicious.

'Okay,' he called from the kitchen. 'You can come in now!'

He'd cooked dinner and bought champagne.

'You know, I've never had a girlfriend on Valentines,' he said.

There was a cheer inside me.

I felt special.

Romance isn't commercial, it's brilliant.

Sunday 15th February

ROSIE TEXTED ME LAST night, 'I had the best Valentine's Day ever.'

She'd got on really well with Pedro at the party but there'd been no mention of him since.

I rang her up, hungry for gossip.

'Oh no, I haven't heard anything from Pedro,' she said, 'I just had a really nice day.'

Pedro clearly wasn't 'the one'. And she didn't seem all that bothered.

Rosie is like that, happy as she is.

'I have other single friends,' the Date said, later, 'but I think she needs to find him by herself.'

He's probably right.

Monday 16th February

I'VE BOOKED A TRAIN ticket up to Cambridge to see the publishers.

'Why don't you talk over the phone?' Mum's lawyer friend asked.

'I want to see them,' I said.

To make sure they are real.

Tuesday 17th February

GEORGE WAS WRITING HIS will at the counter today.

'This is a bit morbid now, isn't it?' he said cheerfully.

Mum was giving him a hand, telling him where to write what.

'I'll have to give you some money for all this,' he said.

But Mum insists she doesn't want anything in return.

He's repaying her in his own way, in doughnuts.

This week there's been a record amount of cakes passing through our door.

It used to be just George but now Maggie has started dropping them in too. There are currently two lemon muffins at the bottom of the stairs.

There was a time when George only brought in Tottenham cakes; he'd drop them off in packs of four.

Tottenham cakes are like breeze blocks covered in pink icing.

Mum eventually cracked.

'I have to tell you something,' she confessed one day, 'we just don't like the pink ones.'

George didn't get it.

'But they come from the bakers next door,' he said.

'I know . . .' Mum winced. 'We love all the other ones . . . it's just the pink ones . . .'

A part of Mum must've regretted speaking out. But somewhere, a land-fill site of pink cakes was growing and she couldn't cope with the idea of such colossal waste.

Now he brings us in doughnuts, mainly iced rings but occasionally other types too.

Today it was three jam doughnuts: one for me, one for Mum and one for Alfie, who's on a diet.

George suddenly looked up from his will.

'Never been a wine drinker meself,' he said. 'But I had a drop the other day and I tell you what, you can really get hooked on that stuff.'

'That's why I've moved to beer,' I said.

'Makes you fat,' Mum said.

'And sherry?' George said. 'How about a nice drop of sherry?'

Mum nodded. 'Yes, sherry's okay.'

Later on, he came back with a bottle of the stuff. We put it besides the lemon muffins and the three doughnuts on the bottom of the stairs. We weren't quite yet ready to take on this new lot.

It wasn't over though.

While Mum was upstairs, Blanche came in. She was slurring her words but I was up for a chat. She once said she was writing a play so I asked her how it was coming along.

'If I write it,' she said, 'It will be a big hit.'

'Great, then do it!'

'A big, big hit. Better than all this rubbish they do on the telly.'

'Fantastic. So finish it and send it off.'

'No,' she said. 'I can't.'

'But . . . Why?'

'Copyright. If I send it off they'll copy it.'

'So you're not going to do it?'

'No.'

She left as another customer rushed in to look at a floor lamp.

While I was switching the lamp on to show him, Blanche opened the door and threw a small box onto the nearest display shelf.

It wasn't just any box; it was a box with the baker's logo on it.

By the afternoon, there were so many edibles at the bottom of the stairs we were in danger of tripping up and breaking our necks.

My local Spanish friend came in with a thermos of coffee.

We'd met through a Moroccan lamp. She'd asked me for a cheeky discount and I'd asked her where she was from. I don't usually give discounts based on nationality but it turned out we'd lived in neighbouring towns in

Spain. I'd given her a couple of quid off and we'd been friends ever since, which is a bonus, because she makes the best coffee.

Oh, what coffee.

It transported me straight back to my days in Barcelona when there was no need for long winded menu boards because coffee was coffee and milk was just milk.

'Ah, what nostalgia!' I sighed

And then I heard a clatter as Mum tripped to avoid the cakes on the stairs.

I turned to my friend and offered her a doughnut.

She started to say no then hesitated.

'*Bueno,*' she shrugged, '*¿por qué no?*'

Why not indeed.

One down, I thought.

And so spreads the sweetness of our little shop.

Wednesday 18th February

THE DATE GOT HIS visa to travel around Europe.

'What about Gambia?' he suggested.

The cheap holiday offer was only valid on a specific set of days.

'Ooh yes!' I cried. 'How exciting!'

I pictured flamingos and red earth.

'I'm away those days so you'll have to cover,' Mum said, ending the dream.

'How about Malta?' the Date asked.

It didn't have the same ring as Africa but I was up for it.

He kept looking.

'Tunisia?'

'Marvellous.'

'Egypt?'

'I've been before but I'd definitely go again.'

I thought I was being quite easy-going but my date suddenly got irritated.

'You don't want to go anywhere!'

I was baffled.

'Just choose a place yourself!' he said, pushing his laptop towards me.

'Uh. Athens?'

He grabbed the laptop back.

'Done!'

So that's that; we're going next week.

Thursday 19th February

THE FAST TRAIN TO Cambridge was cancelled so I got a slow train.

I was happy on the slow train.

When you're on a train there is nowhere else to be but on the train, which is liberating.

I wrote in my orange hard backed notebook. The one Mum got me for my birthday.

It's turning out to be my favourite notebook ever.

I recognised the publisher from her Facebook profile.

I offered her my hand and she hugged me instead, then apologised for her fluorescent cycling jacket.

We had a pub lunch; three people from the publishers and me.

'So, tell us about this book?' she said.

And there was a split second where I went blank.

But then I swallowed my chip, opened my mouth and started talking.

Thursday evening

I HAVE THREE MONTHS to write my book and I'm going to Athens.

And after Athens I'm going to Valencia.

What was I thinking?

Painting Pears took me three YEARS to write, not three months!

'You'll get it done,' everyone says.

But they don't know how slowly I write.

I have to cancel Valencia.

I don't care about the money. I need to get on with this book.

Monday 23rd February

I WAS THINKING FETA cheese, olives, sunshine, the Acropolis, terracotta pots, vine leaves, togas and goats.

Well, it nearly didn't happen because our 4.30 train didn't show up.

That's 4.30 AM; otherwise known as Stupid o'Clock.

The screen finally admitted it had been cancelled twenty minutes later.

We joined the other panicking group of travellers on a bus heading for Blackfriars. One of the travellers knew of an alternative train.

Alternative in the sense it moved backwards.

My heart shrunk with every lethargic chug of that awful train.

I couldn't believe we were going to miss our plane. It was our first international trip together.

Even though our gate was already closed, we still ran to the check-in.

The airport was heaving.

The easyJet queues were swollen.

I slowed down in front of them, breathing fast.

An air steward stepped in front of us.

'Sofia?' he asked.

'No, Emily,' I said.

'Athens!' my date cried.

The steward nodded and waved us ahead of the queues to the check-in desk.

'Close the gate as soon as you've checked in these two,' he said.

Thank Zeus!

Three hours later and we were in unexpectedly messy Athens. There was graffiti all over the place and lots of burnt and boarded up buildings with unfinished roofs.

I wasn't put off though; I was still amazed we'd made it.

'Maybe our hotel is in the ghetto,' my date said, by way of explanation.

It wasn't very sunny either.

It was spitting with rain when we visited the Acropolis and so windy I almost lost my hat.

The Date took amazing pictures. I cut his head off in mine.

There was hardly a tourist in sight even though it turned out to be Carnival.

On Saturday the wigs and party hats came out.

We found a pair of oversized orange sunglasses which boosted our popularity in the bars.

A nonchalant barman in a dressing gown served us up free ouzo shots with cream.

'Markos,' he said, when we asked him his name.

What a hero.

People thought we were locals, perhaps because we both look Mediterranean.

We couldn't understand a word they were saying and communicated with our orange sunglasses instead.

They say travelling with the Date is the big test. But it wasn't really.

The real test on this trip was finding coffee for less than 4 Euros.

Who told me Greece was cheap?

But I suppose it was revealing in some ways.

I now know the Date gets excessively irritated by pigeons.

Thursday 26 February

I'M BACK IN LONDON; back in the shop.

I don't have the holiday blues. In fact I don't want to go on another holiday until I've finished my book.

I'm anxious.

My stomach hurts and everything tastes like toast.

'You've got to learn to let go,' Mum said. 'Worrying won't get it done.'

'You've got to enjoy it,' the Date said.

'I can't enjoy it if I don't have time to do it!' I cried.

But later, while I sat sniffing my sleeve, I realised he was right.

If I didn't enjoy it then there was no point. I may as well just keep on at the shop and let my writer's dream be wiped away with a squirt of Clean n' Fresh window cleaner.

March

⚜

Tuesday 3rd March

I TRIED TO PUT my blog on MySpace last night.

I was trying to be pro-active. You know, go global.

The publishers might only print a few hundred books if I don't prove I can sell more.

By my rough calculations a few hundred won't make me enough to pay for my electric toothbrush. And although it's not about the money I don't want to be working in the shop forever.

I want a bit of independence, that's all; a place of my own where I can hang lights of my choice.

But after two hours it wasn't looking good, my page was still a mess.

I couldn't get the photos to fit the space.

It looked like a take-away menu designed with an Etch-a-Sketch.

I rang my brother for help because his Facebook status read: *I don't get Facebook! MySpace is much better!*

My computer skills were the worst he'd seen.

'Go back to playing with rocks then build up to pen and paper,' he said.

I swore at my laptop, sobbed a little then went to bed and fell asleep sniffing my pillow.

Today I was tired and grumpy.

George brought me in a ginger bread man first thing in the morning.

I don't think all this sugar is helping my anxiety levels but I started nibbling at its head anyway.

I was down to its Smartie belly button when Connie walked in wearing her long burgundy cardigan.

She'd combed and lacquered her hair into a silver chignon. Her nails were bright pink.

'Wow!' I said, 'Where've you been all this time?'

I hadn't seen her for months.

In fact, I was surprised at how relieved I was to see her. I was beginning to wonder if she'd popped off.

'Ginger bread man?' I said, offering her its remaining leg. 'Customers keep bringing me cakes.'

'Because you got nothing on you,' she said, cocking her nose up at the gingery amputation. 'You're like one of them *anorexits*.'

I was expecting her to go on auto pilot after that and tell me about her blood tests, the time they shoved a camera through her groin, every steak and kidney pie she'd ever defrosted and the curtain tiebacks her friend once bought her in Bristol.

'I've had a cold since the 20th December,' she said.

'That's a long time.'

Then she lifted up her top and showed me how the coughing had affected her hernia.

'They think I've split open my stomach,' she said.

I winced. 'Ouch.'

I didn't really understand how she could still be standing with a split open stomach.

'Doesn't it hurt?' I asked

'Of course it hurts. I got a taxi to the doctors, didn't I?'

I got distracted by the white-haired hippie who was gleefully running her fingers through all the crystal.

I wanted to slap her hand.

'Yes, it *is* crystal!' I called out.

That only seemed to egg her on.

'Oh it's lovely,' she gushed, and sent a chandelier into a spin.

I rushed over to stop it, inwardly groaning.

'Can you not do that?'

I tasted the absence of 'please' but I couldn't bring myself to say it.

'Oh sorry!' she cried.

Next she delved into the boxes of odd crystal we were sorting out by the counter. She held one up by the wall then dropped it.

'Oh sorry!' she said again.

Connie rolled her eyes. She doesn't like nonsense.

Actually, I reckon Connie scares a few people.

Not me though. I often feel quite fond of her.

She told me about the curtain tiebacks her friend had bought her once in Bristol.

'I'll bring them in next time,' she said.

I started to tell her I'd already seen them but then changed my mind. One more time won't hurt.

Saturday 7th March

CHILDREN LOVE OUR SHOP. They love it when the sun shines through the crystal and makes rainbows.

'Are they real diamonds?' they ask.

'No,' I say. 'I'd be on holiday if they were.'

They don't understand and stare blankly at me.

'Don't touch nufin',' the younger Mums bark, before the kid's even had a chance to.

The posh Mums have a more laissez-faire attitude. They assume that little two year old Henry will come to the conclusion all by himself that swinging a floor lamp back and forward isn't a clever idea.

'Now darling,' they chide. 'You don't want to be doing that really, do you?'

But that's exactly what they want to be doing otherwise they wouldn't be doing it. So they wobble it with their sticky hands until Mummy and Daddy get flustered and retreat to the cafe next door, where there are crayons and colouring books and other posh toddlers running riot.

Today we felt sorry for a pair of brothers. Their Mum is a regular. She's super strict and makes them wait outside, even if it's freezing cold.

'I don't want you causing trouble,' she always says.

But they are so lovely and well-behaved, I feel like winking at them and telling them they can play tag around the shop if they really want to.

Mum and I looked at each other when we saw them standing outside looking glum, and knew what we were each thinking.

We hung a bead of crystal on fishing twine and gave one each to the boys.

'Hang them in your window and you'll get rainbows all around your room,' we explained.

Their faces lit up with these big beautiful smiles. It was so lovely to see them happy.

'Don't lose them,' their Mum snapped.

You lose them if you want to lose them! I thought.

Some people are no fun.

Monday 9th March

PEOPLE ARE STARTING TO notice we exist.

Some even realise we're closing down.

A few make sympathetic faces at us.

'Oh dear, did the recession get you?'

I know they've only popped in because their friend is in the bakers buying a sausage roll.

'Nope, it didn't get us,' I say. 'We've been meaning to do this for years.'

Then I get the urge to make something up, say we're moving to Peru to breed llamas.

Most of the locals don't believe we're closing down.

Personally I'm no longer certain of anything. I keep saying 'two months'.

'You'll be here next year,' someone said today.

The thing is, what with being noticed, we're finally selling some lights.

It's not enough to warrant opening another check out or putting a 'queue here' sign outside the door.

The only shop that needs one of those signs is the pie an' mash shop.

People are out there at ten in the morning, excited at the prospect of jellied eels.

I don't think I'll ever feel that way about jellied eels.

Having said that, I promised Petra I'd try them before we closed.

I can't back out, especially now that the pie an' mash bloke has smiled at me and said 'good morning' for the first time ever.

I've been waiting all my life for the pie an' mash man to say 'good morning' to me. Every day I pass by him as he leans against the green shutters, smoking an interminable roll up.

I tried to smile at him months ago but he just narrowed his eyes at me.

Now the hostility has truly gone and I feel at ease with the whole street.

Well, nearly.

It's the window cleaner.

I can't help it. Every time I see him I feel irritated.

It's the way he huffs and puffs outside the shop when I haven't put the shutter up.

It's not like I don't put it up on purpose. I have to go onto the street, stop someone in their tracks, interrupt them in their morning routine, to ask them to risk breaking their back pushing up my grimy shutter.

I don't like asking people. It's awkward.

It's even worse when it's pouring with rain.

The window cleaner can't do it because he can't lift his arm, which might be a clue to why he does such a rubbish job of cleaning our windows.

When he arrived I went outside to see if I could get some help.

My only shutter-lifting candidates were two skinny blokes who looks stoned.

I hesitated before I asked the younger of the two.

'What, like this?' he said, and tried and failed to push it up with one arm.

Between us we managed to lift it.

Relieved, I headed back inside and went back to pinning crystal.

After a while I saw the same young bloke talking to the window cleaner.

I got the impression he was asking him for money. As much as I dislike the window cleaner, I felt bad that he might be getting hassled while cleaning my windows.

'Was he asking you for money?' I asked, as he walked through the door.

'What?' he snapped.

I assumed he'd misheard me. Why else would he reply so aggressively?

'That bloke . . . .' I said, 'I wasn't going to ask him to help because he looked a bit spaced out.'

'He was only talking to me!' he cried, missing my concern.

My intention to be friendly started to fail.

'Calm down, I thought he was asking you for money.'

'He wasn't asking me for any money, he was just talking to me.'

'Right. Good. Fine. I just thought he looked a bit spaced out that's all.'

'It's his job!' he cried. 'He's probably tired! He doesn't just sit at the counter taking money all day like you.'

At which point, I completely lost it.

'You have no idea what we do in here!' I yelled.

And then I told him to go.

'You don't need to be like that love,' he smirked. 'Start again, shall we?'

I was seething.

'We can start again next week!' I said, through gritted teeth.

I locked the door and went upstairs after that.

I stood by the boiling kettle and reflected on what had taken place

Sometimes I wonder if we'll ever be able to leave this shop.

Thirty years in existence.

6 months closing down.

No end date.

Is it our destiny to keep struggling on like this?

Or is the window cleaner the key?

If I was able to accept everything about the shop, including the window cleaner, would I be free to go?

Thursday 12th March

THE TIME HAS COME and Rosie and I are packing for Valencia.

Except we're not packing because we both detest packing.

Yes, it seems that Rosie has the same problem as me.

10pm and neither of us were anywhere near started.

17°C in Valencia, apparently.

But what did that really mean?

Rosie rang to say she'd put a load of washing on.

'It will never dry in time,' I told her.

An hour later, I rang her.

'I don't understand,' Rosie said.

'What?'

'When does it come?'

'When does *what* come?'

'You know . . .'the fear'?'

'*What* fear?'

'The fear that time is running out and you really have to pack.'

It was a good question and I thought about it for a moment. Our plane was at midday so we'd have to leave at about 9.30 the following morning.

'I reckon it'll come in about two hours,' I said.

'Mmm,' she said, but I could tell she wasn't convinced.

Friday 13th March

ROSIE TEXTED ME AT 8.30 a.m.

'Ah the fear, the fear has come!'

March — no days, no date, no time!

TIME TO WRITE?

Ha.

Not even a text message.

'Go! Go! Go!' Sergio cried, as my cousin and I chased after him down the streets of Castellón.

Sergio works in Tourism.

I should've known it would be like this.

Action packed.

Informative.

No time for a coffee break or a lazy look around the shops.

We were going to stay with him for a few days before we headed to Valencia where Rosie and I had already planned to see *Las Fallas** (pronounced * fal-yas).

Las Fallas is every pyromaniac's dream.

It's a festival that laughs in the face of health and safety inspectors all over the world; perhaps English ones most of all.

Kids exchange footballs for firecrackers.

Grown-ups smoke beside unlit fireworks.

Monumental sculptures, decorating both city and villages, are sent up in flames.

But Sergio wasn't going to let Castellón be overshadowed by its bigger neighbour.

He was going to make sure we saw every detail of his festival. He promised that one day he would be president and would make it even more spectacular.

'I have projects!' he kept saying, 'lots of projects!'

Sleep had no place in our host's plans. It didn't matter that he didn't drink. He made sure we were in the right place at the right time for every street drinking tradition there was.

So energetic he put the Duracell bunny to shame.

Three hours after we'd crashed into our beds, we were woken with a Latin radio station turned up to breaking point.

'Go! Go! Go!' he shouted.

It was the midday fire cracker show and *Baila La Bamba* on top volume was nothing to the explosions we were about to hear.

'No! Don't cover them!' Sergio said, as our hands rushed to our ears. 'Open your mouths or you'll go deaf.'

The bangs shook our insides as we clung on to each other.

I thought about my date, a sound engineer whose ears were his livelihood.

Rosie thought of her grandparents surviving through the blitz.

But there was no time to dwell on these things.

Onwards we went, to a sun drenched square where everyone drank shots of pink lambrusco and ate monkey nuts.

So many monkey nuts.

Try saying Pamplona with your mouth full of them. In fact try saying Pamplona with your mouth full of anything.

Ah, the things my cousin and I learnt.

We marched to the edge of the city to see artists working on the *Gaiatas*: beautiful hand crafted monuments, six metres high and packed out with flashing light bulbs.

They welcomed us with cava and we got so merry we ended up signing their overalls.

There wasn't one night that we went to bed before six in the morning, or one night I didn't drunkenly text my date back in London.

It was lucky I'd prepared the week's blog beforehand.

Sergio didn't have internet so he took me to his friend's house and waited while I posted it.

But I was so exhausted. I kept reading it through and finding faults with it.

It took me ages.

'I need a siesta,' I told him, on our way back to his house.

'No time!' he said. 'We must go! Go! Go!'

'No, I need a siesta.'

I was going to sleep and no one could stop me.

Back in our room, Rosie was curled up in bed.

I lowered myself onto my mattress on the floor and went to lay my head on my pillow. But I'd misjudged the distance and instead of a soft pillow I banged my head on the chest of drawers behind it. In an instance I was crying my eyes out.

'Oh god, did that really hurt?' Rosie asked suddenly wide awake.

'No,' I sobbed, 'It was the straw that broke the camel!'

And that's when I knew I would crack if we didn't leave Castellón.

The next day we headed to Pego, a small village outside Valencia.

Possibly a Thursday, definitely March

OUR NEXT HOST WAS Josep. He was used to speaking Valencià and spoke Spanish with his mouth half-closed, which sometimes made it hard for me to understand.

He was friendly, quiet and joked about his lack of hair.

Rosie and I had met him while walking on the Camino de Santiago.

We hadn't known what he did for a living until we'd arrived in Santiago and a group of us had met up for a beer.

'Don't tell me, I'll guess,' I'd said. 'You're an accountant?'

I couldn't have been more wrong.

Josep was an artist; a *fallero* artist.

'What are *fallas*?' the foreigners on the Camino wanted to know.

He struggled to explain.

Sculptures, he called them.

Compositions, some as high as five storey buildings, full of colourful figurines that the *fallero artistas* drew, designed, moulded then painted.

But they're more than sculptures. They're illustrations and interpretations of the times, they're stories, busy with characters, meaning and magic.

There are huge *fallas* and *fallas infantiles*.

Josep had spent all year working on his *falla infantil*.

Each *falla* had its own group of supporters, called *falleros*, who dressed up in traditional dress. The blokes smart in black coats and breeches and the girls in elaborate crinoline skirts and princess Leia hair do's.

203

They set up a marquee beside two of the *fallas* and doled out beer and monkey nuts.

The band never slept and our dancing turned into drunken aerobics as the days turned to nights.

At more than one point, Rosie hijacked the drums. I think it might be her calling.

And then on the third day, the group of *falleros* set up a barrier around the two *fallas* outside the marquee.

They wound strips of firecrackers around all those brightly coloured creations and poured petrol over them.

Two fire men turned up, smoking.

The *fallera* queen stepped forward to light the taper.

'Don't do it!' Rosie said.

'You're all crazy!' I said.

And suddenly the firecrackers exploded and fireworks shot into the air and the whole thing went up in flames.

Just like that.

A year's work reduced to ashes.

He hadn't even had his name on his creation.

'The new year starts now,' Josep said, with more than a trace of sadness.

But there was joy too.

It was another opportunity; another chance to do something for the pure love of it.

Monkey Nuts.

But brilliant.

Still March

WE WENT TO JOSEP'S parents' house near the sea.

His dad walked us around the plot of land, showing us the olive trees and vegetable patches.

His Mum cooked a paella with chickpeas, chicken, pork and prawns.

We sat outside in the sun.

No plates, just a fork.

His dad gave us different wines to taste: sweet wine, white wine, red wine.

'No, no,' I said, then tried them all anyway.

'You could stay here and write,' Josep said.

It was bliss.

I didn't want to go back.

I felt distant from my life in London.

Monday 23rd March

I'M BACK IN LONDON, back in the shop.

'Your eyes are small,' Mum said.

'I didn't sleep very much.'

My date surprised us with a visit and we had a panini in the cafe next door.

I suggested we moved to Valencia.

He said he couldn't move until he got his English residency.

'How long left?'

'Three years.'

'Pity.'

And then I thought of my book and realised all I wanted to do was stay where I was and write it.

Saturday 28th March

MY COUSIN, ROSIE, HAD been to yoga and was sitting opposite me at the counter.

Mum was packing up a light nearby.

A woman came in to see the chandelier we'd made for her house in the Caribbean. She was accompanied by a tall young man. He wore a pale pink T-shirt tight over his chest.

Her eyes welled up when she saw her light.

'It's beautiful,' she said.

Our eyes welled up when we saw the young man.

Yes, beautiful, we thought.

And we assumed it was her partner and inwardly congratulated her.

'We were wondering if we should remove the crystal,' Mum said, 'as you're travelling by plane.'

'Yes, I think that would be better.'

Rosie and I started taking off the crystal.

'You can't be,' Mum said, looking at the man. 'I don't want to say this but . . .'

'My son,' said the woman, smiling.

'Not the same one. The last time you came in here, you were with a lit-tle boy.'

'I'm big now,' he said.

Rosie and I giggled behind the chandelier.

'Yes,' the woman said. 'It might've been him or it might've been another son. I have three.'

Three like that?

'Have you seen his guns?' Rosie murmured.

Yes, I had seen his 'guns', the huge muscles in his arms.

The ones in his chest hadn't escaped me either.

I think we'd all noticed them, even Mum seemed a bit distracted.

'Right,' she said, 'where will you put the crystal?'

'Hand luggage,' the woman said.

'Ah, now, it'll come out black on the x-ray so you'll need to have access to it because they'll want to see what it is.'

'Like a load of puff,' said Muscles.

Rosie and I giggled behind the chandelier.

Mum nodded her head then suddenly stopped and frowned.

'No, I don't get it,' she said. 'Like what?'

'Puff,' he said again

Mum looked confused.

'Oh, you mean . . .'

She didn't quite know if what she knew was quite right.

'I don't know about that,' she said, finally.

Rosie and I kept our heads down and finished packing up the crystal.

We put it in a bag. The chandelier frame went in a separate box.

'Now the crystal might be . . .' Mum began then paused to look Muscles up and down. 'Nothing is too heavy for you, is it?'

Rosie and I giggled behind the counter.

'It's not about strength, it's about balance,' he said.

He laughed and almost fell over a box behind him.

Rosie and I giggled some more.

He took the bag and the box, one in each arm and his Mum lead the way out.

'Have a good holiday!' we called after them.

'Take care girls,' he said. 'Have a good one.'

'Come back any time!' Rosie said.

I gawped at her.

'So much for being shy,' I said.

We didn't quite know what to do with ourselves after they'd gone.

For a while we were just three silly shop girls talking about boys.

Sunday 29th March

I ADMITTED TO THE Date that I still hadn't written to the little boy in Guatemala.

'What!' he cried. 'That's terrible! You've sent him nothing? You're awful!'

I didn't expect him to be so outraged and I suddenly felt furious.

It wasn't like I was sitting around doing nothing. I worked all day at the shop then worked all evening on my book.

He had loads of days between jobs and though he might have paperwork to do and emails to write, it wasn't the same as having to physically be somewhere.

'Are you done yet?' he asked, when I paused in my rant.

'Yes,' I said.

But I still felt angry when I got off the phone and sent him a text.

'I think you should remember what it's like to work full-time,' I wrote, 'now I'm done.'

He didn't reply but I felt better. In fact, I was full of energy.

I was going to write to this child once and for all.

I don't know why I hadn't done it yet. I'd been busy but it wasn't just that. It was a strange thing to get my head around, writing to a little boy who lived in a different world to you on the other side of the planet.

I used biro to draw the card. I drew a waving bird, a fat cat, a mummy dog and two puppies playing.

'They look like rats,' Rosie said, about the puppies.

'Chinchillas,' I conceded.

But it all came together when I coloured it in.

The Date texted me something completely unrelated to my moody message. Luckily, he's not the type to hold a grudge. He just moves on.

Anyway, I finally finished the card and then read through the guidelines.

I was supposed to send a gift weighting no more than 150g.

'How much is that?'

'Think of ham,' Mum said.

'How much ham?'

When I read on, I understood that the gift should be bought from their gift catalogue.

'I think I threw it out,' Mum said.

I went onto their website but it didn't help.

It was so frustrating.

In the end Mum and I worked out it was possible to just buy something and send it.

I lay awake for ages thinking about what I would send.

A colouring book would be fun.

Stickers? All kids love stickers.

Maybe even a T-shirt.

How much was 150g?

Monday 30th March

IT WAS MY DAY off today and I was determined to get this package off to Guatemala.

I was also feeling extremely tense because it was my one day off to write and instead I was with the Date looking for a colouring book.

I hadn't seen my date properly since I'd got back from Valencia but despite that, I couldn't enjoy myself. I was there but wasn't there.

I bought a colouring book that was thicker than I wanted. I bought a magic paint book, crayons and colouring pencils.

I left the date feeling like I hadn't really engaged with him at all.

At home, I couldn't find any photos to send to the little boy. I looked everywhere but in every photo I was either with random people, looking crazy, blurred or in bikini.

I was so tired and frustrated, I ended up in tears.

Tomorrow I'll send it without fail.

Tuesday 31st March

I CAN'T WRITE MY book until I've sent this package off to Guatemala.

This evening I had everything spread out across the kitchen table. I'd drawn the card and was now writing the letter in Spanish.

My inner perfectionist was coming out and I kept tearing it up and starting again.

It was ten o'clock by the time I'd written it and it was really short.

After that I started looking for photos again of the whole family.

I found a half-decent one of me but there was a big glass of beer in front of me and someone else's cigarettes.

'They'll think I'm a bad influence.'

'Cut a bit off the bottom,' Mum said.

So I did, but then it looked like a really squat picture.

'You didn't need to cut that much,' Mum said.

'Shall I look for a different picture?'

'No. He's three, I don't think he's going to care what you look like.'

The next hard bit was finding photos of the family.

I just wanted it to look nice.

'If you were an aid worker no one would have a chance,' Mum said. 'By the time you'd decided what colour plate to use, everyone would've died of hunger.'

Midnight came and I was still putting it all together. I bumped into Mum as she came out of the bathroom in her nightie.

'He's 16 now,' she said.

We giggled about that for ages.

Probably because we were tired.

Tomorrow, I'm sending it without fail.

April

❧❦❧

Wednesday 1st April

WE DON'T HAVE A weighing scale in the shop so I couldn't tell if my parcel weighed more than 150g. Mum suggested I go to the vegetable stall, so I did.

Total 365g.

I took out the magic paint book and two paint brushes:

300g

I weighed the colouring book and some crayons:

263g

I weighed the colouring book on its own:

170g

'Just send it,' Mum said.

I put the colouring book and the crayons in the package and left everything else out. I wrote out a cheque to help with the postage costs.

Finally, I went to the post office and sent it.

Thursday 2nd April

I CLEARED MY ROOM this evening because I couldn't find the floor. A small slip of paper fell into my hands. It was from the child sponsorship programme.

It read: *In light of our in-depth research and feedback from the children we work with, we are stopping the process of sending gifts to sponsored children. We found gifts cause jealousy and division within communities.*

Monday 6th April

THAT MAN SELLING THE *Guardian* came in again.

The same one who said he was a 'Volontaire' raising money for 'the children'.

I could have just said 'yes' or 'no' but I decided I should try to get to the bottom of this once and for all.

'I don't get it,' I began.

'Very good news,' he said, turning the pages of the paper he'd placed in front of me. 'Celebrity, sport, fashion . . .'

'I don't mean the paper. I know what the *Guardian* is. I don't get why you're selling them.'

'For the children!' he cried. 'For the church!'

'But why are you selling a newspaper for the church?'

'For the children!'

He was getting exasperated but I wanted an answer.

'Yes but why would the *Guardian* give you free newspapers to sell for the church?'

'I sell them for the children, very cheap price.'

'The same price as the newsagents, I know that but . . .'

My investigation wasn't bearing much fruit and I wasn't sure where I was going wrong.

I zoomed in on his name badge, which as before, wasn't a name badge at all. Actually it was a huge, red piece of card with 'Back Stage Access' on it and the Virgin logo in one corner.

Aha, I thought, feeling clever.

'So, what charity is it?'

'I do it for church!'

'Yes,' I nodded at his card, 'but what charity?'

He looked down at his 'name badge' and held it up.

'They sponsor.'

'Virgin sponsor you to sell the *Guardian* for the children?'

'Yes.'

'That doesn't make any sense. Why would Virgin buy the *Guardian* for you to sell for the children?'

'Yes.'

'I don't get it.'

'I get money for the children!'

'So you say.'

To be honest, I was starting to get on my own nerves.

Why didn't I just give him a break and buy it? It was 90p for god's sake.

And maybe it was for the children. *His* children.

Perhaps it would make sense if I thought about it long enough.

'I just don't get it, that's all,' I said, surrendering a pound.

His face lit up. He tried to give me 10p change.

'Keep it,' I said.

Perhaps he was a victim of the credit crunch. If so, he needed it more than I did.

I still had lots of lights to sell, which was why the shop continued to be open.

People keep noticing the closing sign for the first time and conversation is getting repetitive.

'Oh no you're closing! Why are you closing?'

And we give a long explanation about how we're only shutting the retail, that we're still clearing samples from the factory and that we won't go quickly.

Except today.

Today I kept it short.

'New life,' I said.

The customer was so surprised she didn't know what to say.

'Oh!' she said.

Then because I felt like I'd been too abrupt I ended up giving her the long version as well.

'I'm only browsing,' she said.

So I stopped talking and read my newspaper.

Tuesday 7th April

'OH LOOK, HERE COMES your boyfriend,' Alfie said, looking towards the shop door.

It was the window cleaner.

I'd told Alfie about my little explosion and I think he thought *I* was the nutcase. Which on reflection, maybe I had been.

'I just want to know where he gets the water in his bucket,' I said. 'There's no fountains around here, he can't bring it from home, he doesn't go into a shop and ask, it isn't bottled water . . . where is it from?'

'Well it's a long day, he's gotta 'go' somewhere,' Alfie said.

'Oh yuk . . .'

It would make sense why our windows never look clean though.

Thursday 9th April

IF WE COULD GET back the time we spend explaining to customers why we're closing, we'd probably have a long weekend by now. It would help if we knew when we were closing. I can't say two months for ever.

'Not immediately,' Mum said, 'that's a good one.'

Someone came in after that and I tried it out.

'Not immediately . . .' I said, and they waited for me to go on, which I did. 'It depends on a few factors . . .'

Then I launched into the greatest explanation of all times. And the customer reciprocated with the story of her life, totting up the time we'd spent talking about closing to a week's holiday.

Monday 13th April

A Mrs Winks came in to pay the balance and collect her chandelier.

I didn't recognise her and checked the date on her receipt.

'2001!' I gasped.

'Yes, it's been a while.'

'Eight years.'

'Yes, something like that.'

'No, it has, it's been eight years.'

'I wasn't feeling well.'

I got on the phone to Mum, who directed me to her light which was still packed and ready to go.

I expect she would've left it another 8 years if it hadn't been for our Closing sign.

Mrs Winks is a record but there are plenty of other customers who disappear for long periods of time mid payment.

Like Mr Francis who came this afternoon wanting another light for his house in Ghana.

He's still paying off for the last one after four months.

It's in the backroom in a plastic bag.

Mr Francis is a small, jumpy man with a voice that scratches your eardrums. Not someone you want to get stuck in a lift with.

My heart sank as the routine haggling began. I hadn't had a cup of tea in hours and felt the familiar stirrings of my inner monster.

The chandelier he was after was already a bargain at £199

'Come on, I'm a good customer!' he said.

It's funny how the bad customers say they are good customers and the good customers say nothing.

'There's already a hundred quid off that light.'

'Aaaah!' he cried. 'I want my discount!'

'185 is the lowest I'll go.'

'Come on!'

'You've got a good thing going here,' I said firmly. 'Where else do you get the luxury of paying when you want?'

'Give me it for £150.'

'Nope.'

Connie walked in with her trolley. My dream of a cup of tea dried up.

'I've come from the doctors,' she announced and waved a hand over her swollen belly. 'They say I've got estra . . . estro . . . something or other.'

'Oh,' I said, looking at Mr Francis, who was fidgeting in front of the chandelier. 'That's not good.'

'They're waiting for the results. Here, look at my list of pills.'

She took out some papers from her hand bag and showed me them.

'Come on, how much?' Mr Francis said, feeling neglected.

'185.'

He whined.

Connie looked him up and down with mild disgust.

I felt awkward. Customers shouldn't barter in front of each other.

'I bring the list so I don't have to bring the pill boxes. I can't be bothered with all that,' she continued. 'And I never remember the names of them, do I?'

I needed Mr Francis to make up his mind. I felt like I was being crushed between two heavy boxes.

'Light that one for me,' he said, pointing at a different chandelier.

Please? I thought.

I bashed the ladder against the counter as I brought it out.

'What is it?' Connie said, turning her attention to my agitated customer. She pointed at his original choice. 'Between that one and the one she's lighting?'

Mr Francis stepped from one foot to the other and nodded his head.

I stood at the top of the ladder and plugged the cables into the tester. The chandelier lit up.

It was a bit dusty and didn't sparkle as much as it could've.

'THAT ONE,' she said, pointing back at the first one.

He looked at her with sudden interest.

'Yes, you think? Okay I'll have it.'

I was gobsmacked. I wanted to give Connie a hug.

Mr Francis handed over a deposit for it and I got the receipt book.

'180,' he said.

I wrote £185.

'What a cheek,' she said, after he'd left.

'Yes, the things I have to put up with,' and I settled into a rhythm of crystal pinning while she told me all about the set of saucepans she'd sent off for and the free oven gloves that came with them.

Tuesday 14th April

A LOCAL LAD CAME in to buy some picture frames.

'When are you closing then?'

I glanced at Mum.

'Well,' I said. 'We're closing the retail, not the wholesale.'

'Oh you mean on the internet,' he said.

'No,' I said. 'Not on the internet.'

'Oh.'

'I mean yes, on the internet . . .'

'Right . . .'

'But not to you.'

'Oh,' he said.

We really need a better line. Preferably *before* we close.

Thursday 16th April

THE DATE RANG ME up in the shop. He told me he had some gossip. I love a bit of gossip so I tried to anticipate it until he told me to shut up and listen.

He'd just found out that his ex-girlfriend was going out with one of his best friends.

'Ah,' I said, feeling my body tense against my will. 'That must be weird.'

'Yes it is.'

He could've stopped there but no, he had to continue.

He told me about feeling weird.

Of course I understood. I knew I'd feel weird if my ex was going out with a best friend. But I didn't want to feel weird on his behalf because this was his ex-girl friend. And if he felt weird about her then it was because he still liked her.

I felt confused and angry.

'Why are you telling me this?' I suddenly cried. 'I don't want to know this. You tell someone else this stuff not me. I don't understand why you're telling me this!'

'Fine,' he said.

And it really wasn't fine.

'My sandwich is going cold,' I said, and hung up.

My mind went on overdrive.

He still loved his ex-girlfriend.

They'd only broken up because he'd moved away.

She still visited his mum.

The only time I'd met his mum was on Skype and I'd gone bright red.

Sooner or later they'd come together and rekindle the flames while me and the anonymous best friend would be left out of the picture.

I felt insanely jealous.

I couldn't concentrate on the light I was dressing. It was a square basket chandelier with so many different sized squares.

I couldn't find half the pieces so I couldn't plug into the job.

I tried not to think about it. I told myself he'd forgive my reaction because he didn't hold grudges.

A few hours later I texted him.

'Are we still friends?'

I waited.

No answer.

I called.

No answer.

Then came a text message.

'Yes, but I feel sad how you spoke to me.'

There's nothing worse than someone feeling sad, feeling disappointed in you.

It means you aren't the person they thought you were. You've shown your true colours and they aren't all that vibrant. In fact they're a faded grey, like a pair of pink knickers that have been mixed up in the dark wash.

That's how I felt all day. Like a limp pair of faded, pink knickers.

It was over. Not yet but inevitably. Like every relationship that had gone before.

I started to sink into that feeling of hopelessness, imagined how it would be to be without him.

I turned to mush, like when I have a glass of wine.

I couldn't imagine not being with him.

A pop up window is telling me stop here.

I won't.

I realised whatever it was I was feeling, that it was *my* problem, not his.

It was my weakness, my need for security.

And yes, maybe we would go our separate ways one day, but not yet, not now.

Not without first trying to learn from my reactions.

Instead of going home, I went straight to meet him.

He greeted me with a huge smile and a bear hug. It was as if he'd forgotten I'd ever snapped at him.

'So we're all good?' I asked.

'Of course darr-ling.'

But the heaviness inside didn't leave me.

Friday 17th April

THE BEST CURE TO thinking is to do something practical.

I was in the Ladies toilets of a local pub this afternoon, the same pub where we're soon to be celebrating Nina's hen do.

I'd come to replace the missing crystal on their chandelier.

It's a metre long and hangs across the two cubicles.

My ladder was ready but I was waiting for Miss Tinkle to finish in the loo. I didn't want to alarm her by reaching out across her head.

She sounded like she'd drunk a fair amount.

tinkle tinkle tinkle tinkle . . .

A pint of beer?

tinkle tinkle . . .

Two?

tinkle

Silence.

I tapped my pliers against the rung of my ladder and waited for the flush.

Instead it started again.

tinkle tinkle tinkle tinkle tinkle . . .

The main door opened and another girl came in.

I hadn't anticipated these interruptions and was beginning to worry that the job would take a long time.

The girl eyed my ladder.

'I'm not a pervert. I've just come to put some crystals on the light.'

'If you say so,' she said.

The toilet flushed and Miss Tinkle came out. The second girl went into the cubicle.

'Do you mind if I put them on while you're in there?' I called out. 'I can't see you.'

'Yeah, go on,' she called back, 'as long as you're not a boy.'

So I went up my ladder and awkwardly manoeuvred myself so I could reach the gaps in the chandelier. I couldn't see her but she could see my hands fiddling about above her.

'That looks weird,' she said.

It didn't take long after that and I was glad to get outside into the fresh air.

We do this sort of thing for local customers, turn up to do the fiddly bits.

One local woman still asks after my brother when her halogen bulbs blow.

'Where is the boy?' she'll ask.

And I have to tell her he turned into a man a long time ago and doesn't live in England anymore.

Other jobs are a little grander.

Like the 2 metre tall spiral chandelier we dressed at 8am this morning in a stairwell at South East London's most famous Funeral Directors. It was like entering a country estate; beautifully maintained with its gardens and clock tower. There was a buzz of activity as everyone got on with their jobs for the day, each person in uniform, appropriately dressed for the task at hand.

Their spacious car park was full of gleaming black vehicles.

They were all so smart and shiny that Mum hesitated before going in.

'What are you doing?' I asked her, as she reversed.

'I can't go in there with this car,' she said. 'It's covered in bird's poo.'

'But this is like our van,' I said.

'It still doesn't need to be covered in bird's poo.'

To reach the chandelier we needed two ladders locked together down the stair case and two Polish builders to hold each side.

I climbed to the top and Mum handed me up a string of crystal, one at a time.

There were hundreds of strings, each one a different length. It was going to take a while.

The builders didn't speak much English and watched in silence.

At one point I felt an urge to chat to them.

I'd done four classes of Polish while studying TEFL* (*teaching English as a foreign language*).

I knew how to say 'bread' and 'one sausage'.

But half an hour later I was still wondering how I could put my knowledge to use.

In the end I kept quiet and let the chandelier do all the talking.

Sunday 19th April

I RECEIVED A MAIL from someone in my Facebook blog group.

A certain young Californian with a Photoshop twinkle in his eye.

Please get a life, he wrote, *because the one you're writing about isn't that interesting.*

I was stunned.

I just sat, staring at it.

I'd been feeling rubbish enough as it was and had been acting insecure and pathetic, sniffing my sleeve a lot and waiting for soppy text messages that never came.

This bloke was right, I thought woefully.

I was hardly a lion tamer.

Lunch was a sandwich, not monkey brains.

I didn't get attacked by wild animals on the way to work and if there were any, I could always get the bus.

Yes, I was just a boring little sales assistant who occasionally sold light bulbs.

It was time I wrote something exciting.

Perhaps I could get electrocuted while I was showing someone a light.

Or fall off my ladder onto someone's dog.

Between the electric shock and flattening the dog I'd get a trauma that would leave me without feeling in my fingers.

The dog owner would sue us of our last pound and we'd no longer be able to pay the rent for the shop.

I'd be left at home stringing crystal with my elbows while Mum rebuilt the business from scratch.

I brushed away a tear and read on.

Additionally your relentless messages clog up my Inbox.

'Oh,' I murmured, sinking further into my seat.

Perhaps writing weekly was too much.

Perhaps every two weeks was more than enough.

What if everyone was feeling the same?

I could just write one blog a month if people preferred.

Or perhaps it was best not to write one at all.

No wonder you people lost the Colonies, he continued.

'Oh,' I gasped, 'the colonies.'

I felt confused as well as dispirited.

I wasn't quite sure how he'd drawn this conclusion.

Neither did I know what colonies he was actually talking about.

All I knew was that if this man was right then a lot of historians had wasted a lot of time researching when they could've just read my blog.

And don't bother messaging me back because I'll delete it unread.

What had I done to make him so angry? I wondered. What could I do to pacify him?

And I'm dumping you as one of my groups or blog memberships or fan page or whatever it is that you're inflicting on us.

I just couldn't understand why he was telling me like this.

Why had he waited so long before leaving?

In fact, why had he joined my group at all if my writing so disturbed him.

He ended with the same energy with which he began.

Seriously, you are one of the most uninteresting and mundane people I've ever encountered.

For a while, I sat at my computer wide-eyed.

For a while, the doubting cells fed themselves and multiplied.

I sniffed my sleeve and waited for a soppy text message that wouldn't come.

And then I saw I had a choice.

Monday 20th April

THE CALIFORNIAN HAS LEFT my facebook group.

Current Members: 136

Why is it easier to be upset by the one that left rather than be happy about the 136 that stayed?

Wednesday 22nd April

THE LANDLORD LEFT A message on our house phone.

His son had driven passed our shop and noticed our 'Closing' sign. He reminded us that we had to give him four months notice.

'You can tell him we are closing,' Papa said, 'not closing down. Tell him not to worry.'

Which made me worry.

What did Papa mean? What was his plan?

I don't want to become a 'Closing Down Shop' like the Dress Shop Man suggested.

'What are you going to do if you close?' people ask.

I've been waiting for the shop to close to find out.

Writing will pay for my electric toothbrush refills but what about everything else?

Friday 24th April

MY WRITER FRIEND, SEB, sent me a message on Facebook:

Hi Em

Just saw the Publishers Status Update:

I've 21 weeks to save my business. I'm going on the road . . . . around Britain . . . . to turn things round.

Is this going to affect your book deal? I hope not . . .

I told him I was worried.

I don't want to set alarm bells ringing unnecessarily, he wrote, *but to be brutally honest you should be . . . x*

Fantastic.

So it's back to square one.

The credit crunch has found a way to hurt me after all.

I'm not going to get a book published and I'm going to be working in the shop for eternity.

Sunday 26th April

AAAARGH.

I'm doing it again. Wanting things in boxes; safe, secure, settled.

It's not just the book. I want the Date in a box too.

Ever since that day the Date told me about his ex girlfriend, I've felt disillusioned.

Like everything is precarious and could fall apart at any moment.

And I send text messages wanting a reply I won't get.

It's been hard to work, hard to write.

What do I want?

What do I want him to tell me?

That we'll be together forever?

Because he can't and I can't.

And then I think, let's break up because I don't want to be on this journey if it has to end.

My book is coming along but I'm demoralised because there's no ending.

Mum dragged me to church. I hadn't been in ages.

I came out feeling so sad.

Big fat tears rolled down my cheeks.

I couldn't stop them. It was like all my resistance was melting away.

'Let's go somewhere different,' we'd said over the phone.

So my date and I were meeting at Westbourne Park.

I took the tube.

It was slow.

I found a pen and folded the hymn sheet in half and scribbled all over it.

Sometimes you have to take a train to stop.

To stop the same pattern of thinking, the same routine.

May

∞

Sunday 4th May

I HAVEN'T HEARD FROM the publishers because it's the bank holiday weekend.

Seb wrote: *'Carry on writing as if your life depended on it!'*

And that's exactly what I'm going to do.

Tuesday 5th May

'A WISE MAN IS FALLING down a cliff,' Mum said suddenly, 'and he gets caught on a branch where he sees this strawberry. What a wonderful strawberry, he thinks and he picks it up and eats.'

'Mmm?'

'And he tastes this strawberry and he really enjoys it. What a delicious strawberry, he thinks.'

'Okay.'

'Then the branch breaks and he crashes to the bottom of the cliff.'

'Mmm?'

'Well, that's it,' Mum said, polishing off her own strawberry. 'He's wise because he can live in the present and enjoy each moment.'

Wednesday 6th May

THE DATE DESIGNED BUSINESS cards for me.

He did them in Photoshop.

He put my photo on one side in black and white.

On the other side he put my name and beneath it, in big, 'Writer'.

'Isn't it a bit big?' I worried.

'No. Now you won't take ages explaining what you do.'

Thursday 7th May

LAST NIGHT I POSTED a blog about the hate mail I'd received.

It took me a long time to write.

'Whatever you do, don't criticise your critics,' my brother said. 'I always thank them and say I'll bear their comment in mind.'

So I didn't criticise, I just wrote what he'd said and my reaction.

This morning I was thrilled to see someone had commented on my blog, telling me not to be put off and to keep on writing.

The comments and emails kept coming all day.

I didn't know who many of them were. It was the biggest response I'd ever got from my blog and it filled me with hope and gratitude.

It made me consider how much better it was to be someone that cheered people on rather than pull them back. I don't think this Californian will ever realise how his negativity could've been converted into so much positivity.

Facebook members: 138!

Friday 8th May

IT'S BEEN A DIFFICULT week for independent businesses.

The pub across the road has been boarded up.

'We've been hearing all sorts of reasons why,' confided the owner of the cafe, lowering his voice. 'Infestation of bats, apparently.'

'Bats? I hope we don't get them!'

I'd never seen bats on our road.

'No, not bats! Rats!'

That's just one of the possibilities.

An inside source told me they're refurbishing. But either they've boarded it all up with the builders within or they haven't started yet.

I went to the 'all and everything' African shop to get some disposable table cloths and found a bailiffs notice stuck on the door.

It's sad. The owner could never find anything you wanted but he was a nice guy.

Back at the shop we had our own problems.

A lanky white-haired man strode in with a bottle of white spirit under his arm.

'Now, am I right in thinking you sell hoover bags?'

'Nope, try a few doors up.'

Another man held up a memory card from a camera.

'Photo?'

'Nope, try a few doors up.'

An African man came in carrying a folder.

'Do you do shipping?'

'Nope, but you could try a few doors down.'

Veronica crept up on me on Friday with her endless bags of second hand jewellery.

A more mysterious regular customer had come in only moments before.

He's a Nigerian lawyer and journalist who appears every few years to, in his words, 'monitor' my progress.

'That sounds creepy,' I said. 'I'm going to blog about you now just in case you turn out to be a psycho.'

Lately I've forgotten how I'm supposed to talk to customers.

Veronica ignored the lawyer sitting on the stool by the counter and proceeded to show me her wares.

'I haven't got any money,' I said.

But she passed me the silver earrings anyway. I was surprised to find I really quite liked them.

'You won't see another pair like it,' she said.

A young Australian couple came in and were looking at a chandelier. I'd seen them before and sensed they were probably quite serious about buying. We needed a sale and I wanted to help but between the lawyer in front of me and Veronica at the side, I was locked in.

'Okay, I'll have them,' I said.

I thought by buying the earrings Veronica would go and I'd have a bit more space to sell something of my own.

No such luck.

'Have a look at this necklace,' she said.

'Hang on.'

I squeezed passed her to answer a few of the couple's questions before leaving them to deliberate.

The thing was, the necklace was lovely too.

'Vintage,' she declared.

And cheap.

So I bought the necklace and off she went.

The lawyer stayed where he was.

'Do you want anything?' I asked him

'No.

'Bulbs?'

'No.'

So I left him be and attended fully to the couple.

Then Veronica marched back in with one of those woman's weekly magazines turned to some promotion page.

'Can I use your phone?' she said. 'It's a free number.'

I handed her the phone because it was quicker than not giving it to her.

'There's no dialling tone. Can you have a go?'

'I need to help these customers.'

'Let me try,' the lawyer said.

'No, *she'll* do it for me.'

The couple glanced at each other; confused or worried, I didn't know which.

I expected they'd escape while they still could.

My counter was under siege, I couldn't get in front of it or behind it.

'It's free,' Veronica kept saying. 'I wouldn't ask if it wasn't.'

It was one of those moments when I wondered if my life would ever make any sense.

'We've decided,' the couple said. 'We're going to take it.'

'Great!'

But maybe it doesn't have to.

Monday 11th April

ALFIE CAME IN TO do some repairs.

A lady had left a glass table lamp the week before.

'It's vintage BHS,' she'd gushed when she'd brought it in. 'You wouldn't believe how hard they are to get.'

Mum had taken it out of the box and had inspected the broken lampholder.

'Glorious, isn't it?' the lady had continued, 'You could just eat it couldn't you?'

And Mum had just turned it upside down and looked to see if there was a cord grip. She didn't agree, she didn't say anything and I'd started to feel a bit awkward.

'Yes,' I'd said, to fill the gap. 'It's lovely.'

Alfie looked at it today. He rubbed his nose and stepped away from it. Then he followed the markings on the base with his finger.

'What do they look like to you?' he said.

They were splodges of grey, faint splashes of blue.

'Bruises?'

'Birds poo,' he said, firmly. 'Big bird's poo.'

I looked over at it again.

'Yes, I suppose.'

'Like a sea gull's.'

'Just don't break it. She's very attached to it.'

We see a lot of attachment in the shop.

'Well, what lights do *you* like then?' people say.

And I have to think hard.

'I don't know if I really like lights,' I sometimes say.

Wednesday 13th May

WITHOUT REALISING IT, I missed the 80s.

In fact, I also missed the 90s.

The sun had come out and Rosie, me and the Date were sitting in Primrose Hill. They were trying to include me in a film quiz.

They hummed theme tunes, quoted legendary lines.

'Come on, it's a classic!' my date cried in disbelief, every time I shrugged.

I picked at the grass, nothing remotely near the tip of my tongue.

'Okay, easy one,' the Date said, and breathed into his hand, *'Luke, I am your father.'*

'Star wars?' I said.

They clapped and I felt relieved.

It's not just films it's music too.

Two decades of culture lost to me.

I used to listen to the radio in the shop but stopped when I grew tired of the same old five songs.

Problem is we don't have many CD's in the shop either.

It's lucky we don't mind repetition; it goes well with the crystal pinning.

Last year we played the sound track of the *Motor Cycle Diaries* over and over, until one morning I found a customer had posted three CD's through our letter box.

'Thought you needed a change,' he said when I saw him next.

Mum's didgeridoo music wasn't much of a hit either .

'What the hell is this?' a customer complained. 'It's like having your head drilled out.'

My taste in music is equally suspect.

I love cheesy Latin stuff; the kind of music where the main singer is always dying of love but always lives to write the next song.

When customers come in, I often lower the volume, embarrassed by the lyrics even though they probably wouldn't be able to understand them.

My date introduced me to Spotify.

It's a program that lets you find any music you like at a click of the mouse.

No downloading, no complications.

The only downside is a few advert breaks.

Usually it's just a certain *'Jonathan'* saying, *'Hi from spotify'*, but sometimes it's a bit more.

A fellow twenty-something came into my shop yesterday and as usual, I discreetly turned the music down.

But then it was really quiet.

Too quiet.

So I thought, sod it, better cheesy music than this awkward silence.

I turned the volume back up just as a spotify advert came on.

'We ALL love music, especially in the bedroom . . .'

I panicked, not sure what was coming next and went to switch it off but instead switched it on full blast.

'Say yes to safe sex!'

Great message but not the one I'd planned to give to this young man who was already looking a little nervous.

The silence that followed was even more uncomfortable.

'Oh Spotify,' Velvet said casually, 'I've known about it for ages.'

Typical, another thing I'd missed.

But it was new to Rosie.

'Are you ready?' I said, when I rang her. 'I'm going to give you a gift.'

We've started texting names of songs back and forward.

Perhaps this is how I'm finally going to get some music education.

I wonder why I care so much anyway.

Only last week a customer came in who I hadn't seen in a long time.

'You closing?' he said.

'Eventually.'

'Oh, that's a shame. I enjoy the music in here.'

I grinned and not so discreetly turned the volume up.

Thursday 14th May

THE DATE'S MUM UNDERSTANDS English and has been following my blog.

'She's a big fan,' he said.

We were talking over Facebook chat so he didn't see me blush.

'You're a big thing in Colombia ☺'

I know he just meant his Mum and his sister but I was chuffed.

It's funny to think his Mum knows so much about me through the blog but we've never met.

I want to meet his family. When I do, I'll go red and get my words mixed up.

The Date was suggesting a winter trip to his parents over the phone.

Not Europe, somewhere hot.

I was lying with my head on his chest.

I could hear his Mum's voice faintly.

'Why don't you tell Emily to come?' she said.

The Date squeezed my arm.

I smiled.

Meeting the Date's family, now *that's* a blog I want to read.

Friday 15th May

I WENT UPSTAIRS AND made two cups of tea today.

I don't know why I made two; I was on my own.

I chucked the milk carton in the bin outside and noticed the man from the wig shop, looking cool in sunglasses.

I'd never asked him to put my shutter up before. He seemed the type who'd think it was beneath him. But when I did he was very obliging.

'You need a strong man around,' he said, 'ask me whenever you need help.'

What a find, I thought, and went back to my teas.

The first was weak, the second, cold.

Veronica came in and I realised I'd started something off. She now knows I'm capable of buying her jewellery.

'Mummy not here?'

'Not today.'

She looked slightly disappointed.

'What size are you?'

'What do you mean?'

'I've got a dress here.'

I was blinded as she pulled out this glittering green number, covered top to bottom in sequins.

'Oh, wow,' I said, struggling for words. 'I don't think it's Mum's thing.'

'You try it.'

'I don't think I'd wear it.'

'Just try it.'

'But really, I wouldn't . . .'

'Let's just see how it looks.'

It would only be a moment, I told myself. Veronica wouldn't give up unless I did.

The dress was really heavy.

I stepped into it and pulled it up over my jeans. It was so tight I could hardly move my legs.

It was like being stuck inside a tube of toothpaste.

'Oh yes, it looks gorgeous on you,' Veronica said.

A tube of toothpaste covered in sequins.

The phone rang and I suddenly realised I was in my shop dressed up like a drag queen.

What had I been thinking?

I pulled down the straps as I picked up the phone.

'Is that accounts?' a woman asked.

'Uh . . . accounts is . . . away.'

Veronica came around the counter, right up to me.

'You need to try it on without your top,' she said, and then tried to lift my top off.

The dress stuck around my hips.

'I see,' the woman said.

I wriggled and the dress slid down, pushing my knees together. I fell forward and caught myself on the counter still hanging onto the phone.

The dress dropped around my ankles.

'Do we owe you something?'

'You could wear it to a nice party,' Veronica said.

I pulled my top back down.

'Or a dinner.'

'Yes, I'm afraid so,' the woman said, and gave me the amount.

'Right, I'll sort it out tomorrow.'

'Thank you.'

I hung up and handed the dress back.

'It's not really my style.'

'It's only 20 pounds, it was 150 . . .' Veronica pushed.

I caught myself thinking about Nina's hen party.

'No, really,' I said, gathering my wits. 'It's not me.'

'I know it's a bit over the top,' she said, 'but I think you and your Mum should be a bit more over the top . . .'

'Well . . .'

'I have to say it,' she said. 'I think you're both too conservative.'

This was news.

Was that the impression I gave?

She started getting her bags of jewellery out.

And I don't know how she does it but after she'd gone, I looked at my reflection in the mirror and ran my finger over the new necklace.

It's a blue heart pendent on a gold chain, with a big bling diamante inside it.

And I thought, maybe if I look at it long enough, I'll start to like it.

Sunday 17th May

I TOLD MUM VERONICA said we were too conservative and that we should be more over the top.

'I think she's right,' Mum said.

Which got me thinking it'd be fun to be a bit more eccentric.

'I think we should buy a wig from next door,' Mum said, later.

'What kind?'

'A ginger bob.'

Thursday 21st May

I WENT TO COLLECT my business cards after work.

It was pouring with rain and I didn't know where I was going.

I'm not an umbrella person so I just walked through it, getting soaked. It didn't occur to me to take cover; it didn't look like it would stop anyway.

When I arrived at the printers, the guy put his beer down and went out the back.

He brought back a small box held together with elastic and some lose cards.

'Sorry they're soggy,' I said, handing him the five ten pound notes.

'That's alright love. I hope they were worth getting wet for.'

I looked at my picture; arms folded, trying not to smile.

I turned it over, feeling excited.

There was my name and underneath:

Writer

'Yes,' I said, smiling. 'They were.'

Sunday 24th May

THERE ARE CERTAIN THINGS I have to do before we close the shop:

Eat pie an' mash

Smile at the window cleaner and say, 'What a fantastic job you've done!'

Buy a wig from next door and wear it all day.

Tell the newsagent lady to cheer up.

Tell the dentist lady to cheer up.

Dance in the shop window.

Give someone a coherent reason why we are closing.

Tell someone it's not Art Deco.

Tell a child they are diamonds.

Finish my book.

Have a party in the shop.

Monday 25th May

IT WAS HOT TODAY. A man came in and wandered around the shop with sweat patches under his arms the size of lily pads.

'So when are you closing?' he asked.

'When we can fit all our stock under our bed,' I said.

I was making the crystal for a two metre long chandelier that someone had bought on the weekend. We'd expected business to slow down but it was still going strong.

'Not soon then,' he said.

Later I was going to meet the Date. We were thinking of going to that comedy club where I once hid behind a sofa cushion. A year later and I felt the same excitement and anticipation of seeing him.

The customer fiddled with a price label and scratched his stubble.

'So, what are you going to do when you close?'

I stopped stringing crystal for a moment and looked up at him.

'The same as what I'll do if we don't close,' I said. 'I'm going to write another book.'

THE END